SADLIER

VOCABULARY WORKSHOP®

ENRICHED EDITION

Jerome Sho

Senior Series Consultant

Vicki A. Jacobs, Ed.D.
Associate Director, Teacher Education Program
Lecturer on Education
Harvard Graduate School of Education
Cambridge, Massachusetts

Series Consultants

Louis P. De Angelo, Ed.D.
Associate Superintendent
Diocese of Wilmington
Wilmington, Delaware

John Heath, Ph.D.
Professor of Classics
Santa Clara University
Santa Clara, California

Sarah Ressler Wright, NBCT
English Department Chair
Rutherford B. Hayes High School
Delaware City Schools, Ohio

Carolyn E. Waters, JD, Ed.S.
ELA/Literacy 6–12 Supervisor
Cobb County School District
Marietta, Georgia

Sadlier

Reviewers

The publisher wishes to thank for their comments and suggestions the following teachers and administrators, who read portions of the series prior to publication.

Rivkie Eisen
English Teacher
Ateret Torah High School
Brooklyn, New York

Jennifer Etter
English Dept. Chair
Shorecrest High School
Shoreline, Washington

Eileen Ghastin
English Teacher
John F. Kennedy High School
Bronx, New York

Sheri Goldstein
English Dept. Chair
Ida Crown Jewish Academy
Chicago, Illinois

Claudia Lefkowitz
English Teacher
Central Florida Preparatory
Gotha, Florida

Scott Leventhal
English Teacher, Dept. Chair
Council Rock H. S. South
Holland, Pennsylvania

Jeanne Pellegrino
English Teacher, Dept. Chair
Plantation High School
Plantation, Florida

Jennifer Portilla
English Teacher
Pace Brantley School
Longwood, Florida

Kausam R. Salam, Ph.D.
English Teacher-Dual Credit
Cypress Falls High School
Houston, Texas

Linda Schwartz
English Dept. Chair
Seaford School District
Seaford, New York

Patricia Stack
English Teacher
South Park High School
South Park, Pennsylvania

Barbara Swander Miller
Language Arts Dept. Chair
Cowan Jr/Sr High School
Muncie, Indiana

Stephanie K. Turner
English and French Teacher
St. Ursula Academy
Cincinnati, Ohio

Robert Viarengo
English Dept. Chair
Palma School
Salinas, California

Cover: Concept/Art and Design: MK Advertising and William H. Sadlier, Inc.; Cover pencil: Shutterstock/VikaSuh.
Photo Credits: Interior: age Fotostock: Datacraft 169; ImageSource: 108; Sharon Day: 88 *bottom left.* Alamy/ AF archive: 13 *bottom right*, 107, 155; Antiques & Collectables: 183; Bosiljka Zutich: 79; By Ian Miles-Flashpoint Pictures: 23 *top right*; D. Hurst: 32 *top right*, 33 *bottom right*; DIZ München GmbH, Süddeutsche Zeitung Foto: 55; Europe: 151; Everett Collection: 32 *top left*; Les. Ladbury: 22 *bottom*; North Wind Picture Archives: 173; Paul Rapson: 131; Pictorial Press Ltd: 23 *top left*; Sandra Baker: 27; World History Archive: 117. AP Photo/Bill Allen: 189; Eric Gay: 165 *top.* Art Resource, NY/ SSPL/National Railway Museum: 50 *bottom left*, Adoc-photos: 71 *top left*, 71 *top center*; Fitzwilliam Museum, Cambridge: 113; The Kobal Collection/Paramount: 141; The Kobal Collection/ RKO: 97; The Kobal Collection/Woodfall: 59. Associated Press/Efrem Lukatsky: 51 *top left.* The Bridgeman Art Library /Private Collection: 145; Roger-Viollet, Paris: 70. Corbis/Bettmann: 12 *bottom left*, 31, 33 *top*, 93, 103; Patsy Lynch/Retna Ltd.: 136 *bottom*; Pete Souza/White House: 136 *top*; Reuters: 65; Underwood & Underwood: 75, 185 *top.* Cross-Cultural Solutions: 174 *top right*, 174 *bottom right.* Digital Vision: 126, 126 *background*, 126 *background*; Jay Nicholas: 126 *left*, 126 *center*, 126 *right*, 127 *left*, 127 *right.* Eric Reed: 17. Everett Collection/ United Artists: 41. Getty Images/Paula Bronstein/Stringer: 50 *bottom right*; Photolibrary/Nativestock Pictures: 147 *left*; Time & Life Pictures: 71 *top right*, 135. The Granger Collection, NYC: 61 *left*, 185 *bottom.* The Image Works/ Jim West: 109 *top left*; ©Wesley Bocxe: 109. Lebrecht Music & Arts: 12 *bottom right*, 21. Library of Congress, Prints and Photographs Division: 184; New York Herald: 60 *background.* Mary Evans Picture Library/Ronald Grant Archive: 60. Masterfile: 89 *bottom left*, 98 *bottom left*, 175 *top left*; Robert Harding Images: 179. National Portrait Gallery, London/Elliot & Fry: 22 *bottom right*; Frederick Hollyer: 69. OnAsia/Fadil Aziz: 147 *right.* Photo Researchers/Chris Butler: 165 *bottom*; Roger Harris: 164. Photodisc: 32, 71 *texture.* PhotoLibrary/ Nativestock Pictures: 37. Photoshot/Mohamed Omar: 51 *bottom right.* Shutterstock: donatas1205: 146; Hintau Aliaksei: 12 *bottom left*; javarman: 147 *top*; Lisovskaya Natalia: 175 *bottom right*; nagib: 12 *bottom*; Nixx Photography: 174 *background*; Peter Sobolev: 184 *background*; Phase4Photography: 71 *background*; Robbi: 108; Sharon Day: 88 *background*; Shmeliova Natalia: 165 *bottom*; Vjom: 97–98 *icons.* Timothy Hughes Rare & Early Newspapers: 33 *top right.* Wikimedia Commons: 61 *right*, 193.

Illustration Credits: Tim Haggerty: 46, 79, 122, 160, 198. Zina Saunders: 146.

Address inquiries to Permissions Department,
William H. Sadlier, Inc.,
9 Pine Street, New York, New York 10005-4700.

Printed in the United States of America.
ISBN: 978-0-8215-8013-4
4 5 6 7 8 9 BRR 22 21 20 19 18

For additional online resources, go to vocabularyworkshop.com and enter the Student Access Code: VW12SH2JBK99

ENRICHED EDITION: New Features

For more than five decades, VOCABULARY WORKSHOP has proven to be a highly successful tool for guiding systematic vocabulary growth and developing vocabulary skills. It has also been shown to help students prepare for standardized tests.

New in this edition are the **Reading Passages, Writing, Vocabulary in Context,** and **Word Study** activities. Nonfiction, high-interest passages use 15 or more of the Unit vocabulary words in context. Two writing prompts require a response to the reading and provide practice in writing for standardized tests. New Vocabulary in Context activities present words from the Unit as they are used in classic works of literature. After every three units, Word Study activities, developed in conjunction with Common Core State Standards requirements, provide practice with idioms, adages, and proverbs, as well as denotation and connotation and classical roots.

Look for the new **QR** (Quick Response) codes on the **Reading Passage** and **Vocabulary in Context** pages. The code can be read with a smartphone camera. To read the QR code, download any free QR code application to a smartphone. Snap the code with a smartphone camera to go directly to iWords for the Unit or an interactive quiz. With iWords you can listen to one word at a time or download all of the words in a Unit to listen to them at your convenience.

The new structure of VOCABULARY WORKSHOP is made up of 15 Units. Each Unit consists of the following sections: a **Reading Passage, Definitions, Choosing the Right Word, Synonyms and Antonyms, Completing the Sentence, Writing,** and **Vocabulary in Context**. Together, these exercises provide multiple and varied exposures to the taught words—an approach consistent with and supportive of research-based findings in vocabulary instruction.

Five **Reviews** cover Vocabulary for Comprehension and Two-Word Completions. Vocabulary for Comprehension is modeled on the reading sections of standardized tests, and as in those tests, it presents reading comprehension questions, including specific vocabulary-related ones, that are based on a reading passage.

A **Final Mastery Test** assesses a selection of words from the year with activities on Synonyms, Antonyms, Analogies, Two-Word Completions, Supplying Words in Context, Word Associations, and Choosing the Right Meaning.

In each level of VOCABULARY WORKSHOP, 300 key words are taught. The words have been selected according to the following criteria: currency and general usefulness; frequency of appearance on recognized vocabulary lists; applicability to, and appearance on, standardized tests; and current grade-level research.

ONLINE COMPONENTS

vocabularyworkshop.com

At **vocabularyworkshop.com** you will find iWords, an audio program that provides pronunciations, definitions, and examples of usage for all of the key words presented in this level of VOCABULARY WORKSHOP. You can listen to one word at a time or, if you wish, download to an MP3 player all of the words of any given Unit. You will then be able to listen to the audio program for that Unit at your convenience.

At **vocabularyworkshop.com** you will also find **interactive vocabulary quizzes, flashcards, games and puzzles** that will help reinforce and enrich your understanding of the key words in this level of VOCABULARY WORKSHOP.

CONTENTS

iWords Audio Program available at **vocabularyworkshop.com**.

VOCABULARY STRATEGY: Using Context

The **context** of a word is the printed text of which that word is part. By studying the word's context, we may find **clues** to its meaning. We might find a clue in the immediate or adjoining sentence or phrase in which the word appears; in the topic or subject matter of the passage; or in the physical features—such as photographs, illustrations, charts, graphs, captions and headings—of a page itself.

The **Vocabulary in Context**, **Vocabulary for Comprehension**, and **Choosing the Right Meaning** exercises that appear in the Units, the Reviews, and Final Mastery Test provide practice in using context to decode unfamiliar words.

Three types of context clues appear in the exercises in this book.

A ***restatement clue*** consists of a *synonym* for or a *definition* of the missing word. For example:

In his _______________ , the little horse could easily clear a five-foot stone wall, but now that those prime years are over, he is retired to pasture.

a. heyday **b.** bravado **c.** fustian **d.** opportunist

In this sentence, *prime years* is a synonym of the missing word, *heyday*, and acts as a restatement clue for it.

A ***contrast clue*** consists of an *antonym* for or a phrase that means the opposite of the missing word. For example:

"My opinion on the situation may be far too rigid," I admitted.

"On the other hand, yours may be too (**malleable, contumelious**)."

In this sentence, *rigid* is an antonym of the missing word, *malleable*. This is confirmed by the presence of the phrase *on the other hand*, which indicates that the answer must be the opposite of *rigid*.

An ***inference clue*** implies but does not directly state the meaning of the missing word or words. For example:

"A treat for all ages," the review read, "this wonderful novel combines the _______________ of an expert with the verbal skill and artistry of a masterful _______________."

a. fustian . . . hauteur
b. jeremiad . . . pastiche
c. rapport . . . zealot
d. acumen . . . raconteur

In this sentence, there are several inference clues: (a) the word *expert* suggests *acumen*; (b) the words *novel, verbal skill,* and *artistry* suggest the word *raconteur*. These words are inference clues because they suggest or imply, but do not directly state, the missing word or words.

VOCABULARY STRATEGY: Word Structure

Prefixes, **suffixes**, and **roots**, or **bases**, are word parts. One strategy for determining an unknown word's meaning is to "take apart" the word and think about the parts. Study the prefixes and suffixes below to help you find out the meanings of words in which they appear

Prefix	**Meaning**	**Sample Words**
com-, con-	together, with	compatriot, contact
de-, dis-	lower, opposite	devalue, disloyal
il-, im-, in-, ir, non-, un-	not	illegal, impossible, inactive, irregular, nonsense, unable
super-	above, greater than	superimpose, superstar

Noun Suffix	**Meaning**	**Sample Nouns**
-acy, -ance, -ence, -hood, -ity, -ment, -ness, -ship	state, quality, or condition of, act or process of	adequacy, attendance, persistence, neighborhood, activity, judgment, brightness, friendship
-ant, -eer, -ent, -er, -ian, -ier, -ist, -or	one who does or makes something	contestant, auctioneer, resident, banker, comedian, financier, dentist, doctor
-ation, -ition, -ion	act or result of	organization, imposition, election

Verb Suffix	**Meaning**	**Sample Verbs**
-ate	to become, produce, or treat	validate, salivate, chlorinate
-fy, -ify, -ize	to cause, make	liquefy, glorify, legalize

Adjective Suffix	**Meaning**	**Sample Adjectives**
-al, -ic,	relating to, characteristic of	natural, romantic
-ful, -ive, -ous	full of, given to, marked by	beautiful, protective, poisonous

A **base** or **root** is the main part of a word to which prefixes and suffixes may be added. On the Classical Roots page of the Word Study section, you will learn more about Latin and Greek roots and the English words that derive from them. The following lists may help you figure out the meaning of new or unfamiliar words.

Greek Root	**Meaning**	**Sample Words**
-cryph-, -crypt-	hidden, secret	apocryphal, cryptographer
-dem-, -demo-	people	epidemic, democracy
-gen-	race, kind, origin, birth	generation
-gnos-	know	diagnostic
-lys-	break down	analysis

Latin Root	**Meaning**	**Sample Words**
-cap-, -capt-, -cept-, -cip-	take	capitulate, captive, concept, recipient
-cede-, -ceed-, -ceas- -cess-	happen, yield, go	precede, proceed, decease, cessation
-fac-, -fact-, -fect-, -fic-, -fy-	make	faculty, artifact, defect, beneficial, clarify
-tac-, -tag-, -tang-, -teg-	touch	contact, contagious, tangible, integral
-tain-, -ten-, -tin-	hold, keep	contain, tenure, retinue

For more prefixes, suffixes, and roots, visit **vocabularyworkshop.com**.

VOCABULARY AND READING

Word knowledge is essential to reading comprehension. Your knowledge of word meanings and ability to think carefully about what you read will help you succeed in school and on standardized tests, including the SAT, the ACT, and the PSAT.

New **Reading Passages** provide extra practice with vocabulary words. Vocabulary words are boldfaced to draw students' attention to their uses and contexts. Context clues embedded in the passages encourage students to figure out the meanings of words before they read the definitions provided on the pages directly following the passages.

Students read excerpts from classic literature in the **Vocabulary in Context** exercises. Each excerpt includes one of the Unit vocabulary words as it is used in the original work. Students can use what they learn about the word from its use in context to answer questions on the definition.

The **Vocabulary for Comprehension** exercises in each review consist of a nonfiction reading passage followed by comprehension questions. The passages and questions are similar to those that you are likely to find on standardized tests.

Kinds of Questions

Main Idea Questions generally ask what the passage as a whole is about. Often, but not always, the main idea is stated in the first paragraph of the passage. You may also be asked the main idea of a specific paragraph. Questions about the main idea may begin like this:

- The primary or main purpose of the passage is. . .
- The passage is best described as. . .
- The title that best describes the content of the passage is. . .

Detail Questions focus on important information that is explicitly stated in the passage. Often, however, the correct answer choices do not use the exact language of the passage. They are instead restatements, or paraphrases, of the text.

Vocabulary-in-Context Questions check your ability to use context to identify a word's meaning. Use line references to see how and in what context the word is used. For example:

- **Hoi polloi** (line 8) is best defined as. . .
- The meaning of **folderol** (line 30) is. . .

Use context to check your answer choices, particularly when the vocabulary word has more than one meaning. Among the choices may be two (or more) correct meanings of the word in question. Choose the meaning that best fits the context.

Inference Questions ask you to make inferences or draw conclusions from the passage. These questions often begin like this:

- It can be inferred from the passage that. . .
- The author implies that. . .
- Evidently the author feels that. . .

The inferences you make and the conclusions you draw must be based on the information in the passage. Your own knowledge and reasoning come into play in understanding what is implied and in reaching conclusions that are logical.

Questions About Tone show your understanding of the author's attitude toward the subject of the passage. Words that describe tone, or attitude, are "feeling" words, such as *indifferent, ambivalent, scornful, astonished, respectful.* These are typical questions:

- The author's attitude toward . . . is best described as. . .
- Which word best describes the author's tone?

To determine the tone, pay attention to the author's word choice. The author's attitude may be positive (respectful), negative (scornful), or neutral (ambivalent).

Questions About Author's Technique focus on the way a text is organized and the language the author uses. These questions ask you to think about structure and function. For example:

- The final paragraph serves to. . .
- The author cites . . . in order to . . . .

To answer the questions, you must demonstrate an understanding of the way the author presents information and develops ideas.

Strategies

Here are some general strategies to help you as you read each passage and answer the questions.

- Read the introduction first if there is one. The introduction will provide a focus for the passage.

- Be an active reader. As you read, ask yourself questions about the passage—for example: What is this paragraph about? What does the writer mean here? Why does the writer include this information?

- Refer to the passage when you answer the questions. In general, the order of the questions mirrors the organization of the passage, and many of the questions include paragraph or line references. It is often helpful to go back and reread before choosing an answer.

- Read carefully, and be sure to base your answer choices on the passage. There are answer choices that make sense but are not based on the information in the passage. These are true statements, but they are incorrect answers. The correct answers are either restatements of ideas in the text or inferences that can be drawn from the text.

- Consider each exercise a learning experience. Keep in mind that your ability to answer the questions correctly shows as much about your understanding of the questions as about your understanding of the passage.

WORKING WITH ANALOGIES

A verbal analogy expresses a relationship or comparison between sets of words. Normally, an analogy contains two pairs of words linked by a word or symbol that stands for an equals (=) sign. A complete analogy compares the two pairs of words and makes a statement about them. It asserts that the relationship between the first—or key—pair of words is the same as the relationship between the second pair.

In the **Analogies** exercises in the Final Mastery Test, you will be asked to complete analogies—that is, to choose the pair of words that best matches or parallels the relationship of the key, or given, pair of words. Here are two examples:

1. maple is to **tree** as
  a. acorn is to oak
  b. hen is to rooster
  c. rose is to flower
  d. shrub is to lilac

2. joyful is to **gloomy** as
  a. cheerful is to happy
  b. strong is to weak
  c. quick is to famous
  d. hungry is to starving

In order to find the correct answer to exercise 1, you must first determine the relationship between the two key words, **maple** and **tree**. In this case, that relationship might be expressed as "a maple is a kind (or type) of tree." The next step is to select from choices a, b, c, and d the pair of words that best reflects the same relationship. The correct answer is (c); it is the only pair whose relationship parallels the one in the key words: A rose is a kind (or type) of flower, just as a maple is a kind (or type) of tree. The other choices do not express the same relationship.

In exercise 2, the relationship between the key words can be expressed as "joyful means the opposite of gloomy." Which of the choices best represents the same relationship? The answer is (b): "strong means the opposite of weak."

Here are examples of some other common analogy relationships:

Analogy	Key Relationship
big is to **large** as **little** is to **small**	**Big** means the same thing as **large**, just as **little** means the same thing as **small**.
brave is to **favorable** as **cowardly** is to **unfavorable**	The tone of **brave** is **favorable**, just as the tone of **cowardly** is **unfavorable**.
busybody is to **nosy** as **klutz** is to **clumsy**	A **busybody** is by definition someone who is **nosy**, just as a **klutz** is by definition someone who is **clumsy**.
cowardly is to **courage** as **awkward** is to **grace**	Someone who is **cowardly** lacks **courage**, just as someone who is **awkward** lacks **grace**.
visible is to **see** as **audible** is to **hear**	If something is **visible**, you can by definition **see** it, just as if something is **audible**, you can by definition **hear** it.
liar is to **truthful** as **bigot** is to **fair-minded**	A **liar** is by definition not likely to be **truthful**, just as a **bigot** is by definition not likely to be **fair-minded**.
eyes are to **see** as **ears** are to **hear**	You use your **eyes** to **see** with, just as you use your **ears** to **hear** with.

There are many different kinds of relationships represented in the analogy questions you will find in the Final Mastery Test, but the key to solving any analogy is to find and express the relationship between the two key words.

*Read the following selection, taking note of the **boldface** words and their contexts. These words are among those you will be studying in Unit 1. As you complete the exercises in this unit, it may help to refer to the way the words are used below.*

Fascinating Rhythm: The Life of George Gershwin

<Biographical Sketch>

It is no exaggeration to say George Gershwin (1898–1937) composed some of the most exciting, original, and popular music of all time: Songs that have become standards, like "I Got Rhythm," "Embraceable You," and "Someone to Watch Over Me," plus more than two dozen Broadway shows and film scores—including *Funny Face, Shall We Dance?* and *Of Thee I Sing*—and dazzling orchestral pieces and jazz compositions. Not bad for a poor Brooklyn kid who dropped out of high school.

Gershwin, born Jacob Gershvin in New York to Russian-Jewish immigrants, displayed a precocious talent for piano playing and studied with a master teacher who gave him a classical foundation. At age 15, he resisted the **hidebound** restrictions that school placed on his time and talents and left it for good. His parents, perhaps realizing George's remarkable musical potential, had a **laissez-faire** attitude: Maybe their son was destined for greater things?

Young George got a job as a song plugger on Tin Pan Alley for the princely sum of $15 a week. (A song plugger demonstrated new songs to promote the sale of sheet music. Tin Pan Alley was the name given a New York street where Manhattan-based music publishers and songwriters congregated.) His rise was swift. His first hit was the somewhat **ribald** "When You Want 'Em, You Can't Get 'Em, When You've Got 'Em, You Don't Want 'Em." But then he and lyricist Irving Ceaser wrote "Swanee," which was recorded by popular entertainer Al Jolson and took the country by storm, selling more than two

Piano music from *Porgy and Bess*, 1935

George Gershwin, 1937

million records. After that, success seemed a done deal, a **fait accompli**. It allowed him to escape the **hierarchy** of the music business and forge his own career path, on his own terms.

In the productive 1920s and 1930s, Gershwin wrote countless pieces, including the jazz-influenced "Rhapsody in Blue" and music for the groundbreaking folk opera *Porgy and Bess*. His music became a **bellwether** for the dramatic changes in American popular music. To create an **adjunct** to his Broadway work, he started writing for the movies. In light of his classical and theatrical background, some in Hollywood thought Gershwin too highbrow or too **oblivious** to the realities of scoring a movie. But he was quickly able to win skeptical moviemakers over, and many became not just fans but **proselytes** of his music.

Gershwin's main musical collaborator was his lyricist brother, Ira, but he also had fruitful **quasi**-partnerships with several others, including Kay Swift, a trailblazing American woman composer. But such luck was not to last. In 1937, after complaining of headaches and other symptoms that left him feeling **effete**, Gershwin was diagnosed with a brain tumor. He collapsed during a concert and lay **supine** on the floor. Doctors operated, but he died in July of that year at just 38 years of age. Ira, grief-stricken, floundered in a **morass** of self-pity. How could he go on writing without his beloved brother and partner? But Ira eventually teamed up with other composers, including Jerome Kern.

George Gershwin's stellar reputation has only grown since his death. Singers from Frank Sinatra to Sting have recorded his songs; and films, TV shows, and commercials utilize his music. In the early 1950s, the Oscar-winning musical-comedy film *An American in Paris* featured many Gershwin songs and musical **vignettes** plus an elaborate, **chimerical** dance sequence created around Gershwin's symphonic tone poem, which remains one of his best-known works.

iWords™

Snap the code, or go to **vocabularyworkshop.com**

Gene Kelly and Leslie Caron, *An American in Paris*, 1951

Note the spelling, pronunciation, part(s) of speech, and definition(s) of each of the following words. Then write the word in the blank spaces in the illustrative sentence(s) following. Finally, study the lists of synonyms and antonyms.

1. adjunct (aj′ ənkt)

(*n.*) something added to something else as helpful or useful but not essential; an assistant or helper; a valuable quality or characteristic; (*adj.*) added or connected in a subordinate capacity; attached to a faculty or staff in an auxiliary capacity

The test manual was an ____________________ provided free with purchases of the new textbook series.

An ____________________ art professor will be hired.

SYNONYMS: (*n.*) associate, addition, accessory

2. bellwether (bel′ weth ər)

(*n.*) the male sheep that leads the flock to the slaughterhouse; a leader, as in a desperate or violent undertaking; an indicator of trends

When their ____________________ was captured, the mob disbanded.

SYNONYMS: ringleader, initiator, barometer
ANTONYMS: follower, imitator, emulator

3. caterwaul (kat′ ər wôl)

(*v.*) to howl or screech like a cat; to quarrel; (*n.*) a harsh or noisy cry; a racket

The desperate survivors ____________________ about their suffering.

The ____________________ in the alley kept us awake.

SYNONYMS: (*v.*) whine; (*n.*) screech

4. chimerical (ki mer′ i kəl)

(*adj.*) absurd; wildly fantastic; impossible

They proposed yet another ____________________ get-rich-quick scheme.

SYNONYMS: visionary, quixotic, pie-in-the-sky
ANTONYMS: realistic, down-to-earth, practicable

5. effete (i fēt′)

(*adj.*) lacking in wholesome vigor or energy; worn-out or exhausted; sterile or unable to produce; out-of-date

The ____________________ society was once a thriving and vigorous one.

SYNONYMS: decadent, enfeebled
ANTONYMS: thriving, burgeoning, vigorous, dynamic

6. fait accompli (fe ta kôm plē′)

(*n.*) an accomplished and presumably irreversible deed, fact, or action

The proud generals confidently declared the fall of the rebel stronghold a ____________________.

SYNONYM: accomplished fact

7. hidebound (hīd′ baůnd)

(*adj.*) narrow-minded and rigid, especially in opinions or prejudices; stubbornly and unthinkingly conservative

The ____________________ administrator stood by the outdated ways of previous administrations.

SYNONYMS: intolerant, inflexible

ANTONYMS: open-minded, tolerant, progressive, liberal

8. hierarchy (hi′ ə rär kē)

(*n.*) any system of things or people arranged or graded one above another in order of rank, wealth, class, etc.

Within the governmental ____________________, the voice of the junior senator was not a powerful one.

SYNONYM: chain of command

9. laissez-faire (lesā fe(ə)r′; lezā)

(*adj.*) a philosophy or practice characterized by a usually deliberate abstention from direction or interference, especially with individual freedom of choice and action

Ms. Yee's English class had a ____________________ atmosphere, so students worked at their own pace and helped each other.

SYNONYMS: noninterventional, nonrestrictive, hands-off

10. liturgy (lit′ ər jē)

(*n.*) a religious service or rite; the form of a ritual or other act of public worship

The ____________________ has been modernized.

SYNONYM: observance

11. morass (mə ras′)

(*n.*) a patch of low, soft, wet ground; a swamp; a confusing situation in which one is entrapped, as in quicksand

After several bad performances, the aging athlete wallowed in a ____________________ of self doubt.

SYNONYM: bog

ANTONYMS: solid ground, bedrock, terra firma

12. noisome (noi′ səm)

(*adj.*) offensive or disgusting; foul-smelling; harmful or injurious

The ____________________ atmosphere of the slaughterhouse overwhelmed the visitors.

SYNONYMS: fetid, noxious, vile, loathsome

ANTONYMS: wholesome, sweet-smelling

13. oblivious
(ə bliv′ ē əs)

(*adj.*) forgetful; unaware

The hikers were ____________________ of danger ahead.

SYNONYM: insensible; ANTONYMS: aware, cognizant, mindful, alert

14. poltroon
(pol trün′)

(*n.*) a base coward

The ____________________ was caught deserting.

SYNONYMS: craven, dastard, "chicken"
ANTONYMS: stalwart, gallant

15. proselyte
(pros′ ə līt)

(*n.*) a convert; a disciple

The zealous ____________________ rallied in the square.

SYNONYMS: novice, neophyte
ANTONYMS: master, teacher, guide, guru

16. quasi
(kwā′ zī) *or*
(kwä′ zē)

(*adj.*) resembling but not actually being; seemingly but not actually or completely

They formed a ____________________ partnership.

SYNONYMS: kind of, as if
ANTONYMS: totally, completely, actually, in fact

17. raillery
(rā′ lər ē)

(*n.*) good-humored ridicule; teasing

The good-natured ____________________ in the locker room pleased the coach.

SYNONYM: persiflage

18. ribald
(rib′ əld)

(*adj.*) irreverently mocking; coarse, vulgar, or indecent in language

The actor tells ____________________ stories about life in the theater world.

SYNONYM: risqué
ANTONYMS: seemly, proper, decorous

19. supine
(sü pīn′)

(*adj.*) lying flat on one's back; listless or lethargic; apathetic or passive

The hiker relaxed in a ____________________ position.

SYNONYMS: prone, prostrate; inert
ANTONYMS: upright, erect, perpendicular, vertical

20. vignette
(vin yet′)

(*n.*) a short description or sketch; a picture or illustration with edges that gradually shade off; a decorative design on the title page of a book or at the beginning or end of a chapter

All enjoyed the writer's ____________________ of country life.

SYNONYMS: thumbnail sketch, anecdote
ANTONYMS: epic, full-length treatment

Choosing the Right Word

*Select the **boldface** word that better completes each sentence. You might refer to the selection on pages 12–13 to see how most of these words are used in context.*

1. Martin Luther King, Jr. appealed to his countrymen to abandon the (**noisome, hidebound**) stereotypes of racism and rise to a new level of understanding.

2. Financial analysts carefully watch the performance of certain stocks, which they regard as (**bellwethers, vignettes**) for indications of economic trends.

3. How can you expect a prompt response from an agency that is bogged down in a veritable (**morass, liturgy**) of unnecessary red tape?

4. By late imperial times, centuries of soft living had turned the once hardy Romans into an (**oblivious, effete**) and indolent people.

The Martin Luther King, Jr. National Memorial was the first built to honor an American who was not president.

5. We have lived to see the acceptance and enactment of reform programs that, when first proposed, were dismissed as absolutely (**chimerical, oblivious**).

6. The great historian Edward Gibbon sought to explain how and why the (**proselytizing, liturgical**) efforts of the early Christian church met with such extraordinary success.

7. A policy of (**quasi, laissez-faire**) economics makes sense in a textbook, but certain governmental regulations and oversight are necessary in a mixed economy.

8. Overly sensitive to any suggestion of ridicule, young Rogers seemed to be hurt even by a friend's good-natured (**raillery, proselytes**).

9. The lyrics of the song, presented as though they were devastating wit, were in my opinion no more than a coarse and (**supine, ribald**) jest.

10. They have confronted us not with a theoretical possibility but with a(n) (**adjunct, fait accompli**); now we must decide what we can do about it.

11. He is so (**ribald, hidebound**) in his political views that he won't even listen to opinions that differ from his own.

12. Her unfailing courtesy to others is not a mere (**adjunct, morass**) of her personality; it reflects the essential values and standards by which she lives.

13. Failure to stand up for your rights is not being "prudent" or "moderate"; it is the behavior of a (**poltroon, bellwether**).

14. Almost incredibly, a formidable resistance movement had been organized by people whom we had always associated with (**supine, noisome**) submission to authority.

15. I am willing to listen to any reasonable grievances you may have, but this constant (**caterwauling, hierarchy**) about trivia has exhausted my patience.

16. A superintendent is at the head of the (**hierarchy, vignette**) of educators responsible for the schooling of our children and young people.

17. With penetrating insight and a marvelous ear for dialogue, the author gave us in a few words an unforgettable (**adjunct, vignette**) of a confused but hopeful adolescent.

18. After a brief period of popularity, their cheap and vulgar novels lost their appeal and sank into well-deserved (**proselyte, oblivion**).

19. As I listened to the talk of those unlettered people, suffused with love and reverence, I felt that their simple words were a (**raillery, liturgy**) worthy of respect.

20. Although the old senator no longer holds any public office, her fame and prestige are so great that she is still regarded as a (**quasi, hidebound**) public figure.

21. The (**adjunct, supine**) form of the sculpted figure suggests that the artist is interested in revealing—and drawing attention to—life's peaceful moments.

22. (**Ribald, Noisome**) vapors from the manufacturing plant contributed to the overwhelming public outrage concerning disposal of waste in the community.

23. As the family set up their tent, a distant (**caterwauling, poltroon**) of an unseen and mysterious creature sent the children running for the comfort of their parents' arms.

24. A lauded short story writer and novelist, Ernest Hemingway was far from (**effete, ribald**), as he also thrived in such endeavors as bullfighting, hunting, and skiing.

25. Hiking in the woods, we came upon an expansive and impassable (**caterwaul, morass**).

Choose the word from this unit that is the same or most nearly the same in meaning as the ***boldface*** *word or expression in the phrase. Write that word on the line. Use a dictionary if necessary.*

1. has a **fanciful** notion of what the future holds ____________
2. a **coward** we want to avoid ____________
3. a steady stream of **banter** ____________
4. shocked by the **foul** atmosphere ____________
5. startled by the sudden **wail** ____________
6. embarrassed by the **bawdy** prose ____________
7. tempted by the idea of **semi-**retirement ____________
8. recognized the **irreversible situation** ____________
9. unfamiliar with the **ceremony** ____________
10. at the pinnacle of the **pecking order** ____________

Antonyms

*Choose the word from this unit that is most nearly opposite in meaning to the **boldface** word or expression in the phrase. Write that word on the line. Use a dictionary if necessary.*

1. faced with **derision** and contempt ____________________
2. soothed by the **pleasant** odor ____________________
3. **informal proceedings** in the public square ____________________
4. the **whimper** of the unhappy child ____________________
5. enjoyed a deserved reputation as a **hero** ____________________

Completing the Sentence

From the words in this unit, choose the one that best completes each of the following sentences. Write the word in the space provided.

1. A handful of self-appointed "leaders" served as the ____________________ who induced the mob to surge through the barriers.

2. Ever since she learned of the failure of her project, she has been mired in a(n) ____________________ of disappointment and self-recrimination.

3. The use of English rather than traditional languages in religious ceremonies is evidence of efforts to modernize and revitalize the ____________________ of various denominations.

4. Advocates of equal rights maintain that we must reject the ____________________ prejudices that bar the physically impaired from many occupations.

5. The rigid king dismissed as a mere ____________________ anyone who refused to join in his crusade against the forces of evil.

6. Polluted by the spill from a nearby chemical plant, the once beautiful lake had become a foul pool, ____________________ and hideous.

7. She used talent, charm, energy, and determination to fight her way up the corporate ____________________ until she attained the highest position in the company.

8. As late as the seventeenth century, researchers called "alchemists" devoted their lives to the pursuit of ____________________ schemes for turning iron into gold.

9. The baby-sitter had a ____________________ manner about him, so the children got to stay up late when he was in charge.

10. As a rule, I am not a particularly proud or combative person, but I cannot be ____________________ to the fact that you have deliberately insulted me.

11. Their youthful enthusiasm for literature had degenerated over the years into a(n) ______________ preoccupation with quibbling criticism and minor details.

12. Failure in itself is no disgrace, but the ______________ acceptance of failure certainly is.

13. I detected an undertone of hostility and ridicule in the remarks, which were ostensibly no more than good-natured ______________.

14. If you think that the literature of earlier ages was always staid and proper, take a look at some of the ______________ stories in the *Decameron*, written more than 600 years ago.

15. Taking advantage of the young man's naïve idealism, they sought to make him a(n) ______________ to serve in their revolutionary plots.

16. The local Parents' Association has on many occasions served as a willing ______________ to the administration and staff of our school.

17. I think that the critic was a little harsh when he observed that the band's lead vocalist did not sing so much as ______________.

18. The newspaper published my Aunt Alice's series of charming ______________—brief sketches of the town she grew up in.

19. I regret Fred's resignation as much as anyone, but I think that we must regard it as a(n) ______________ and find someone to take his place.

20. As the Smithsonian Institution is only partly under the control of the United States government, it is considered a(n) ______________ governmental institution.

Writing: Words in Action

1. Look back at "Fascinating Rhythm: The Life of George Gershwin" (pages 12–13). Consider the key events of Gershwin's life and the circumstances and personal qualities that contributed to his success. Write a descriptive essay that explains why you think Gershwin was able to achieve so much by the age of 38, using at least three details from the passage and three unit words.

2. George Gershwin had both great talent and great fortune. Is it fortune or talent that is more consequential in a person's life? In a brief essay, explain your opinion with specific examples from your studies, reading (refer to pages 12–13), or personal observations and experience. Write at least three paragraphs, and use three or more words from this unit.

*The following excerpts are from novels by Charlotte Brontë. Some of the words you have studied in this unit appear in **boldface** type. Complete each statement below the excerpt by circling the letter of the correct answer.*

1. Discovering gradually that a wonderful sense of fatigue resulted from these conscientious efforts, I began to reflect whether I might not dispense with that great labor, and concluded eventually that I might, and so sank **supine** into a luxury of calm ... (*Villette*)

To be **supine** is to be

a. recumbent
b. upright
c. anxious
d. alluring

2. These women are incomprehensible. They have the strangest knack of startling you with unpleasant surprises. Today you see them bouncing, buxom, red as cherries, and round as apples; tomorrow they exhibit themselves **effete** as dead weeds, blanched and broken down. (*Shirley*)

Someone who is **effete** is

a. coarse
b. obedient
c. debilitated
d. accomplished

3. I stopped, intimidated and trembling. What a miserable little **poltroon** had fear, engendered of unjust punishment, made of me in those days! I feared to return to the nursery, and feared to go forward to the parlor; ten minutes I stood in agitated hesitation; the vehement ringing of the breakfast-room bell decided me; I *must* enter. (*Jane Eyre*)

A **poltroon** is NOT

a. agitated
b. confident
c. neurotic
d. cowardly

Charlotte Brontë's *Shirley*, first published in 1849, takes place in Yorkshire in the early 1800s.

4. Provided with a case of pencils, and some sheets of paper, I used to take a seat apart from them, near the window, and busy myself in sketching fancy **vignettes**, representing any scene that happened momentarily to shape itself in the ever-shifting kaleidoscope of imagination ... (*Jane Eyre*)

A **vignette** is a

a. map
b. kind of boat
c. depiction
d. good-humored joke

5. Excitement instantly seized the whole party: a running fire of **raillery** and jests was proceeding when Sam returned. (*Jane Eyre*)

Raillery is

a. antagonism
b. storytelling
c. justification
d. joshing

Snap the code, or go to
vocabularyworkshop.com

Read the following selection, taking note of the ***boldface*** *words and their contexts. These words are among those you will be studying in Unit 2. As you complete the exercises in this unit, it may help to refer to the way the words are used below.*

The Code-breakers of Bletchley Park

<Historical Nonfiction>

"They were my geese that laid the golden eggs and never cackled." Thus did British Prime Minister Winston Churchill, with a touch of **paternalism**, describe the code-breakers who worked at Bletchley Park during World War II. Churchill's geese were indeed crucial to the war effort. Maintaining rigorous secrecy about their work, they produced high-level intelligence that had a profound impact on Allied strategy and success.

A tranquil estate tucked into the countryside some fifty miles northwest of London, Bletchley Park stood far from the **melee** and devastation of the war, and remained, with one minor exception, beyond the **purview** of Nazi air raids. The property had been acquired for the British government in 1938, not long before the war's outbreak, under the **aegis** of Admiral Sir Hugh Sinclair, chief of the British intelligence service. To maintain secrecy, the first government visitors to the site **obfuscated** the true nature of Sinclair's interest in the property, claiming to be members of a hunting party. No doubt the rural setting lent a certain **verisimilitude** to their pretense.

Code-breakers and support staff moved into the Bletchley Park mansion in August 1939. Analysts immediately set to work deciphering German communications, with special focus on codes produced by the German's Enigma cipher machines, which were notoriously difficult to break. British intelligence officials were **sanguine** about their prospects, however, having been lately **apprised** of Polish cryptologists' success in the task.

Bletchley Park's main decryption establishment, Buckinghamshire, England; Alan Turing, the most successful code breaker, 1951

Engima Machine in use by German Soldiers during World War II

The Enigma ciphers were electro-mechanical rotor machines, superficially resembling old-fashioned typewriters, that encrypted messages by scrambling alphabetical letters in complex sequences. Used correctly, Enigma codes were practically impossible to break. But seemingly **minuscule** departures from correct procedure could make transmissions vulnerable to analysis by expert cryptologists. Ultimately, it was human error on the part of the German operators of the Enigma machines that let British analysts break the codes.

Bletchley Park analysts, many of whom were academics **deracinated** from British universities, waged war against the Enigma machines armed with expertise in mathematics and linguistics. Some were selected for extraordinary skill at solving crossword puzzles. Others were polyglots familiar with the **lexicons** of various languages. After the United States entered the war in 1941, Americans began to join the staff. Far from **polarizing** the place, American personnel worked comfortably alongside the **indigenous** Britishers who constituted the effort's nucleus. Perhaps the most famous and successful cryptanalyst at the site was Alan Turing, now widely regarded as the father of computer science.

Ultra—the code-name given to intelligence produced at Bletchley Park—made significant contributions to Allied victories at sea and on land, providing information about enemy troop positions, movements, and plans. Ultra informed the Allies of the exact location of all but two of the 58 German divisions on the Western front on D-Day on June 6, 1944.

With the war over, Churchill remarked to King George VI, "It was thanks to Ultra that we won the war." But the strict secrecy maintained about the program, even decades after the war's end, prevented the full story of the contribution made at Bletchley Park from becoming public knowledge. The men and women who served there, those geese that never cackled, had vowed to remain silent about their work. No **lachrymose** farewells saw these staffers off to duty, no **claques** of admirers cheered them as they returned home. It was only in the late twentieth century that the extent of their contribution to the Allied victory was publicly acknowledged.

Snap the code, or go to
vocabularyworkshop.com

Definitions

Note the spelling, pronunciation, part(s) of speech, and definition(s) of each of the following words. Then write the word in the blank spaces in the illustrative sentence(s) following. Finally, study the lists of synonyms and antonyms.

1. aegis (ē′ jis)

(*n.*) protection; patronage; sponsorship

The arts and education programs of the United Nations are under the ____________________ of UNESCO.

SYNONYM: auspices

2. apprise (ə prīz′)

(*v.*) to inform of; to make aware of by giving oral or written notice

The spokesperson will ____________________ us of the latest developments.

SYNONYM: acquaint
ANTONYMS: keep secret, withhold information

3. bibulous (bib′ yə ləs)

(*adj.*) fond of or inclined to drink; absorbent

The retired sailor was a ____________________ old codger.

SYNONYM: inebrious
ANTONYMS: abstemious, temperate

4. claque (klak)

(*n.*) a group of people hired to applaud a performer or performance; enthusiastic or fawning admirers; an opera hat

The soprano's ____________________ was in attendance, as usual.

SYNONYMS: fan club, flatterers
ANTONYMS: critics, detractors, slanderers

5. deracinate (di ras′ ə nāt)

(*v.*) to pull up by the roots; to root out, uproot, or dislocate; to eliminate all traces of

One way to ____________________ prejudice from our society is to heighten public awareness.

SYNONYMS: extirpate, eradicate, expunge
ANTONYMS: implant, nurture, foster, instill

6. exegesis (ek si′ jē sis)

(*n.*) an explanation or critical interpretation (especially of a text)

The newest ____________________ of Abraham Lincoln's presidency purports to be the final word on the subject.

SYNONYMS: analysis, explication
ANTONYM: mystification

7. indigenous
(in dij′ ə nəs)

(*adj.*) originating in the country or region where found, native; inborn; inherent

Grizzly bears and mountain lions are two examples of wildlife ____________________ to the Rocky Mountains.

SYNONYMS: endemic, domestic, homegrown
ANTONYMS: foreign, alien, exoteric, imported

8. lachrymose
(lak′ rə mōs)

(*adj.*) given to tears or weeping; causing to shed tears; mournful, lugubrious

It was a ____________________ tale of poverty and woe.

SYNONYMS: tearful, doleful, dolorous
ANTONYMS: dry-eyed, merry, hilarious

9. lexicon
(lek′ sə kən)

(*n.*) a dictionary of a language; the special vocabulary of a person, group, or subject; a compendium

The ____________________ of computer technology is large and growing.

SYNONYMS: wordbook, glossary

10. melee
(mā′ lā)

(*n.*) a confused struggle; a violent free-for-all; a tumultuous mingling

Many fans were hurt in the ____________________ that followed the soccer match.

SYNONYMS: fracas, brawl, scuffle, donnybrook
ANTONYMS: friendly chat, peace and quiet

11. microcosm
(mī′ krə kos əm)

(*n.*) a miniature world or universe; a group or system viewed as the model of a larger group or system

The ocean liner is a ____________________ of society in the novel *Ship of Fools.*

SYNONYMS: epitome, world in little
ANTONYMS: macrocosm, cosmos, totality

12. minuscule
(min′ əs kyül)

(*adj.*) very small, tiny; (*n.*) a lowercase letter

I ate only a ____________________ portion of the dessert.

In the typeface that the poet chose, every letter used in the poem is a ____________________.

SYNONYMS: (*adj.*) infinitesimal, insignificant
ANTONYMS: (*adj.*) huge, massive, monumental

13. obfuscate
(ob′ fə skāt)

(*v.*) to darken or obscure; to confuse or bewilder

The pedantic lecturer's long-winded explanation served only to ____________________ the meaning of the thesis.

SYNONYM: muddy the waters
ANTONYMS: elucidate, explicate, clarify

14. paternalism (pə tûr′ nə liz əm)
(*n.*) the policy or practice of treating or governing people in the manner of a father dealing with his children

The President won over the worried populace with his attitude of kind ____________.

SYNONYMS: benevolence, solicitude, fatherliness

15. polarize (pō′ lə rīz)
(*v.*) to cause to concentrate around two conflicting or contrasting positions; to cause light to vibrate in a pattern

The debate served to ____________ public opinion on the issue.

SYNONYMS: split, alienate, estrange
ANTONYMS: unite, unify, reconcile

16. purview (pər′ vyü)
(*n.*) the range, extent, or scope of something; in law, the scope or limit of what is provided in a statute

The subject was outside the ____________ of the mayor's authority.

SYNONYM: orbit

17. sanguine (saŋ′ gwin)
(*adj.*) having a ruddy complexion; of a naturally cheerful, confident, or optimistic outlook

Scientists remain ____________ about the chances of finding a cure for the deadly disease.

SYNONYMS: flushed, rosy
ANTONYMS: bloodless, ashen, pessimistic, gloomy

18. solecism (sol′ ə siz əm)
(*n.*) a substandard or ungrammatical usage; a breach of etiquette; any impropriety or mistake

One common ____________ is "irregardless."

SYNONYMS: misusage, blunder

19. vassal (vas′ el)
(*n.*) a person under the protection of a feudal lord to whom he or she owes allegiance; a subordinate or dependent; a servant; (*adj.*) subservient

The duke's ____________ was forced to fight for the king, to whom the duke owed allegiance.

As a ____________ nation, India provided troops for British armies.

SYNONYMS: (*n.*) minion; (*adj.*) servile
ANTONYM: (*n.*) overlord

20. verisimilitude (ver ə si mil′ ə tüd)
(*n.*) the quality of appearing to be true, real, likely, or probable

The play's ____________ won praise from critics.

SYNONYMS: realism, lifelikeness, authenticity

Choosing the Right Word

*Select the **boldface** word that better completes each sentence. You might refer to the selection on pages 22–23 to see how most of these words are used in context.*

1. From the observatory atop the Empire State Building, the pedestrians on the streets below look as (**sanguine, minuscule**) as ants.

From 1931 to 1972, the Empire State Building was the world's tallest building.

2. Even the public opinion polls, which showed a strong trend toward our candidate, did not make us overly (**indigenous, sanguine**) about our chances of winning.

3. Those later scenes, in the opinion of many critics, had so much self-conscious pathos that they lacked conviction and (**verisimilitude, microcosm**).

4. For many years, Americans and Europeans tended to ignore the highly developed (**deracinated, indigenous**) cultures of the peoples of Africa.

5. Their standards are so rigid and so devoid of a sense of proportion that they elevate every minor (**lexicon, solecism**) to the level of a major crime.

6. Falstaff, as conceived by Shakespeare, is not just a (**lachrymose, bibulous**) old braggart but an archetype of human appetites and joy in living.

7. Is it any wonder that the young quarterback is getting a swelled head when he seems always to be surrounded by a(n) (**claque, aegis**) of fawning admirers?

8. It is not enough merely to push aside our prejudices and pretend they don't exist; we must (**deracinate, apprise**) these evils from our minds and personalities.

9. At rush hour, I always have a hard time fighting my way through the (**melee, claque**) of tired commuters scurrying through the station.

10. Morality is not a criterion that can be used to judge whether or not a word belongs in a (**microcosm, lexicon**) of the language in which it is used.

11. Under the American system of personal liberty, there are many aspects of daily life that are not within the (**claque, purview**) of any governmental authority.

12. A(n) (**lexicon, exegesis**) of Virginia Woolf's work reveals that she is an exceptionally modern writer concerned with the psychology and emotion of her subjects.

13. I came to resent the company's (**solecism, paternalism**) because it assumed that employees lacked the self-reliance to take care of themselves.

14. Please do not try to (**apprise, obfuscate**) your responsibility in this matter by irrelevant criticisms of other people's behavior.

15. A basketball team will be sent to the Far East under the (**claque, aegis**) of the State Department to play native teams in various countries.

16. The movie started off well, but the later scenes, with the young heroine slowly dying of a mystery disease, became overwrought and (**bibulous, lachrymose**).

17. If we disregard the emotions and desires of other groups in our area, we are simply going to increase partisanship and (**deracinate, polarize**) the whole community.

18. I think it was very inconsiderate of her to wait until this late date before she (**apprised, obfuscated**) us of her intention to quit the class show.

19. In the tragedy that overtakes the pathetic Lennie in *Of Mice and Men*, we see in (**microcosm, purview**) the cruelty and injustice that pervade our society.

20. Compared to today's free agents, the ballplayers of yesteryear were practically the (**lexicon, vassals**) of the team owners.

21. Thankfully, the beach towels are extremely (**lachrymose, bibulous**), and they were able to control the spread of water due to the bucket that tipped over in the back of the van.

22. When light from the sun hits the surface of the pond, the light is (**indigenous, polarized**), and then we see mysterious reflections on the placid water.

23. The grandmother was impressed by the child's (**sanguine, obfuscated**) complexion and generally healthy appearance.

24. Some call our city a cosmopolitan melting pot of cultures, but my grandparents from Eastern Europe felt (**apprised, deracinated**) and even apprehensive at times.

25. As a (**vassal, bibulous**) state, its citizens had few rights and were subject to others' whims.

Synonyms

*Choose the word from this unit that is the same or most nearly the same in meaning as the **boldface** word or expression in the phrase. Write that word on the line. Use a dictionary if necessary.*

1. the **alcoholic** patron of the local saloon ____________________
2. within the **jurisdiction** of the sheriff ____________________
3. neglected to **notify** the townspeople ____________________
4. the **hangers-on** waiting by the stage door ____________________
5. using the programmers' **special vocabulary** ____________________
6. a **menial** in the royal family's service ____________________
7. to **divide** voters' sympathies ____________________
8. commits a **faux pas** at every turn ____________________
9. an **interpretation** of Joyce's *Ulysses* ____________________
10. a **model** of the entire park ____________________

Antonyms

*Choose the word from this unit that is most nearly opposite in meaning to the **boldface** word or expression in the phrase. Write that word on the line. Use a dictionary if necessary.*

1. the **universe** of the nursing profession ________________
2. **correct usage** essential in a cover letter ________________
3. invited all their **teetotaling** relatives ________________
4. always had to obey the **master** ________________
5. **obfuscation** of the leader's ideas ________________

Completing the Sentence

From the words in this unit, choose the one that best completes each of the following sentences. Write the word in the space provided.

1. Surprisingly, the white potato, which I have always associated with Ireland, is ________________ to the Americas.

2. Is the expression "It is me" to be regarded as a(n) ________________ or as an acceptable idiomatic form?

3. A hard-line speech may gain the congressperson the applause of her followers, but overall it will ________________ sentiments throughout the country and impair national unity.

4. The goal of this course in world history is ________________; therefore, we will carefully examine primary texts from the time periods we study.

5. The issue is basically a simple one, and your efforts to ________________ it by raising endless technical objections will have no effect on us.

6. My classics professor was compiling a complete ________________ of the Latin language.

7. Both sides let on that the negotiators were still miles apart, when in fact the distance that separated their opinions was ________________.

8. ________________ from their Old World environments, European immigrants had difficult adjustments to make.

9. When South Korea was invaded, the United States organized a collective defense effort under the ________________ of the United Nations.

10. If you are ever to get out of this tangled mess, now is the time for action, not indulgence in ________________ self-pity.

11. A case of that type, which does not involve a federal law or constitutional issue, does not come within the ____________________ of the Supreme Court.

12. The third period was marred by a bench-clearing ____________________ that left the hockey rink littered with discarded gloves and sticks.

13. She defended her policy of hiring a(n) ____________________ by noting that even with a supportive audience, someone is needed to get the applause started.

14. He came to realize that the inner city in which he had been raised was a(n) ____________________ of the sufferings of impoverished people all over the world.

15. I am not given to undue optimism, but the preliminary results of the polls make me ____________________ about the outcome of the election.

16. "The rash and ____________________ behavior of that young hothead almost cost us the battle, to say nothing of the war," the general remarked sourly.

17. Without expressing opinions, simply ____________________ us as promptly as possible of the results of the conference.

18. No matter how fantastic and far-fetched the themes of Ray Bradbury's stories may be, he seems able to achieve an extraordinary effect of ____________________.

19. At the outset of World War II, Lithuania lost its sovereignty and became an unwilling ____________________ of the Soviet Union.

20. The people of this underserved area need a program that will "help them to help themselves"—not a form of ____________________ that will make them completely dependent on outside aid.

Writing: Words in Action

1. Look back at "The Code-breakers of Bletchley Park" (pages 22–23). Suppose that you are a member of the British government during World War II, and you need to convince other officials to increase funding to the code-breakers at Bletchley Park. Write a persuasive essay, using at least three details from the passage and three unit words, to explain your reasoning.

2. In times of war, soldiers must be courageous on the battlefield—and their countrymen do not hesitate to praise them for this perceived courage. Do you think the code-breakers at Bletchley Park were equally courageous? In a brief essay, explain your opinion with specific examples from your studies, reading (refer to pages 22–23), or personal observations and experience. Write at least three paragraphs, and use three or more words from this unit.

Vocabulary in Context

Literary Text

*The following excerpts are from works by Edgar Allan Poe. Some of the words you have studied in this unit appear in **boldface** type. Complete each statement below the excerpt by circling the letter of the correct answer.*

1. A pistol fired might suffice to **apprise** them that something wrong had occurred; but the report could not possibly inform them that their only prospect of safety lay in getting out of the harbor forthwith ... (*Narrative of Arthur Gordon Pym*)

To **apprise** means to

a. make aware **c.** revise
b. make nervous **d.** confuse

2. The expanse of the green turf was relieved, here and there, by an occasional showy shrub ... or, more frequently, by a clump of geraniums blossoming gorgeously in great varieties. These latter grew in pots which were carefully buried in the soil, so as to give the plants the appearance of being **indigenous**. ("Landor's Cottage")

Something is **indigenous** if it is

a. unique **c.** native
b. cheerful **d.** mournful

Edgar Allan Poe, father of the modern detective story

3. Piles of death-furniture floundered about. Jugs, pitchers, and carboys mingled promiscuously in the **melee**, and wicker flagons encountered desperately with bottles of junk. ("King Pest")

A **melee** is a

a. tiny model **c.** organized stack
b. giant container **d.** confused mass

4. About noon, as nearly as we could guess, our attention was again arrested by the appearance of the sun. It gave out no light, properly so called, but a dull and sullen glow without reflection, as if all its rays were **polarized**. ("MS. Found in a Bottle")

Polarized rays are those that are

a. reddish **c.** darkened
b. divided **d.** magnified

5. But something too much of these merely personal details, which, after all, are of little importance. I will content myself with saying, in addition, that my temperament is **sanguine**, rash, ardent, enthusiastic—and that all my life I have been a devoted admirer of the women. ("The Spectacles")

A **sanguine** temperament is one that is NOT

a. confident **c.** depressed
b. relaxed **d.** impatient

Snap the code, or go to **vocabularyworkshop.com**

*Read the following selection, taking note of the **boldface** words and their contexts. These words are among those you will be studying in Unit 3. As you complete the exercises in this unit, it may help to refer to the way the words are used below.*

Charles Ponzi and His Scheme

<Informational Essay>

Charles Ponzi was not the first **mountebank** who used a "Ponzi scheme" to swindle investors out of money, and he wasn't the last. But his success, though fleeting, was so great, that it is only natural that schemes of his sort have come to bear his name.

Charles Ponzi

Ponzi emigrated from Italy in 1902 to start a new life in Boston, at first working odd jobs separated by **interstices** of unemployment. Before long he'd landed a job as a restaurant dishwasher and quickly worked his way up to become a waiter—only to be fired for shortchanging customers and stealing. That sad anecdote epitomizes the **macrocosm** of Ponzi's life: He may have been willing to work hard, but he wouldn't **condescend** to work honestly. He snatched at any chance for an easy fortune, his **rapacity** leading him from one half-baked scam to another, from one **enclave** of rogues to another, and from one prison to another. Along the way, the inveterate two-bit hustler somehow managed to **cozen** thousands of unwary investors out of millions of dollars. But even his greatest success as a scam-artist quickly wound up in failure.

It was postage stamps that made Ponzi an **icon** and immortalized his name. In 1919, he began telling people that he'd found a way to pay for United States postage stamps overseas and sell them for a profit in the U.S., taking advantage of currency fluctuations after World War I. Ponzi's trade in postage may have sounded good in theory, but **pragmatic** considerations made it impossible for the plan to yield big profits. If Ponzi knew that his story was full of holes, he didn't show it. Instead, he played the role of a **virtuoso** investor. Relying on his true **forte**, the con man made the most of his charisma, his knack for small-talk, flattery, and **persiflage**, and his flair for stretching the truth. He convinced thousands of people to invest their money with him and promised he could double their money in 90 days. Ponzi wasn't the only person in America who wanted to make a quick buck, and a **plethora** of investment money came pouring in.

What attracted so many investors to Ponzi's scam is that it seemed to be paying off, because when early investors wanted to cash out, Ponzi would simply give them money he had received from new investors. In truth, there was no

PONZI PLACED UNDER ARREST

Boston Man Called Advertising Catspaw for International Group.

RECEIVERSHIP IS ASKED

Run on the Boston bank that held the money invested in Ponzi's scheme

underlying investment, no genuine return. Ponzi didn't bother to put his investors' money into postage stamps or anything else that might actually yield a substantial profit—he was just robbing Peter to pay Paul, while skimming a tidy sum for himself. When people saw the incredible rate of return that investors with Ponzi seemed to achieve, more investors came running. Monkey see, monkey do.

As Ponzi's reputation grew, the authorities became increasingly **quizzical** about his apparent success. The *Boston Post* began to investigate, and when the newspaper spilled the beans, Ponzi's operation was shut down and its mastermind was brought up on charges. It may have been **therapeutic** for his former investors to hear that he'd landed penniless in jail, but to most of them Ponzi's fate must have been an **ancillary** concern: Those who stayed with Ponzi till the end lost more than 70 cents on the dollar when the scam collapsed.

As punishment for his crimes, Ponzi spent over ten years in prison. He was deported in 1934 and died a lonely and destitute man. Few people today remember Charles Ponzi or the crimes that he committed a century ago, but his name lives on. At least that's something, Mr. Ponzi.

Snap the code, or go to **vocabularyworkshop.com**

Note the spelling, pronunciation, part(s) of speech, and definition(s) of each of the following words. Then write the word in the blank spaces in the illustrative sentence(s) following. Finally, study the lists of synonyms and antonyms.

1. ancillary
(an′ sə ler ē)

(*adj.*) subordinate or supplementary

The aide serves in an ____________________ position.

SYNONYMS: auxiliary, accessory
ANTONYMS: central, key, primary, principal, main

2. bowdlerize
(bōd′ lə rīz)

(*v.*) to remove material considered offensive (from a book, play, film, etc.)

The writers refused to ____________________ the book when they turned it into a screenplay.

SYNONYMS: purge, expurgate

3. condescend
(kon di send′)

(*v.*) to come down or stoop voluntarily to a lower level; to deal with people in a patronizing manner

The fashion designer ____________________ to speak to reporters.

SYNONYM: talk down to

4. cozen
(kəz′ ən)

(*v.*) to trick; to cheat or swindle

Some taxi drivers ____________________ unsuspecting tourists.

SYNONYMS: dupe, deceive, beguile, inveigle

5. enclave
(en′ klāv)

(*n.*) an enclosed district, region, or area inhabited by a particular group of people or having a special character

The mountains afforded the displaced townspeople and the local militia an ____________________ of resistance.

SYNONYMS: island, subgroup

6. forte
(fôrt) *or* (fôr′ tā)

(*n.*) a person's strong point; what a person does best

Although I love listening to piano music, playing the instrument is not my ____________________.

SYNONYMS: gift, aptitude, specialty
ANTONYMS: weakness, foible

7. gratis
(gra′ tis)

(*adj.*) free; (*adv.*) without charge

The food provided was ____________________.

During the filming, a local restaurant provided meals to the crew ____________________.

SYNONYM: (*adj.*) on the house

8. icon
(ī′ kän)

(*n.*) a representation or image of a sacred personage, often considered sacred itself; an image or picture; a symbol; a graphic symbol on a computer monitor display; an object of blind devotion

The museum's exhibit of ____________________ included several from czarist Russia.

SYNONYM: emblem

9. interstice
(in tər′ stis)

(*n.*) a small, narrow space between things or parts of things

Once it slipped through the ____________________ in the fence, the rabbit headed straight for the vegetables.

SYNONYMS: gap, slot, crevice, interval, lacuna

10. macrocosm
(mak′ rō koz əm)

(*n.*) the universe considered as a whole; the entire complex structure of something

During the course of their college educations, many students study the economic ____________________.

SYNONYMS: cosmos, entirety
ANTONYMS: model, miniature, microcosm

11. mountebank
(mau̇n′ tə baŋk)

(*n.*) a trickster or swindler; a charlatan

The ____________________ who sold surefire remedies for every imaginable ailment was finally exposed.

SYNONYMS: impostor, quack
ANTONYMS: dupe, "mark," "pigeon"

12. paean
(pē′ ən)

(*n.*) a song of praise, joy, or triumph

The audience responded with a ____________________ of exultation when the ceremony ended.

SYNONYMS: ode, anthem
ANTONYMS: dirge, elegy, threnody

13. persiflage
(pər′ sə fläzh)

(*n.*) lighthearted joking, talk, or writing

The friends engaged in ____________________ from the moment their reunion began until the last of them left.

SYNONYMS: banter, jesting, badinage

14. plethora (pleth′ ə rə)

(*n.*) overfullness; superabundance; superfluity

The inquisitive journalists besieged the harried celebrity with a ____________________ of personal questions.

SYNONYMS: surplus, glut, excess
ANTONYMS: shortage, paucity, dearth, scarcity

15. pragmatic (prag mat′ ik)

(*adj.*) concerned with practical considerations or values; dealing with actions and results rather than with abstract theory; stiff in one's opinions

The mayor takes a ____________________ approach to the city's problems.

SYNONYM: down-to-earth; ANTONYMS: impractical, visionary

16. quizzical (kwiz′ i kəl)

(*adj.*) puzzled; mocking; odd; equivocal

The politician's unexpected comment left all who heard it with ____________________ expressions on their faces.

SYNONYMS: peculiar, perplexed, mystified, derisive
ANTONYMS: unequivocal, unambiguous

17. rapacity (rə pas′ ə tē)

(*n.*) inordinate greed; the disposition to obtain one's desires by force, extortion, or plunder

With the ____________________ of a shark, the ruthless new company went after its competitors' clients.

SYNONYMS: avarice, cupidity, voraciousness
ANTONYMS: liberality, altruism

18. schism (siz′ əm) *or* (skiz′ əm)

(*n.*) a formal split within a religious organization; any division or separation of a group or organization into hostile factions

What began as a disagreement over a minor issue led to a bitter ____________________ within the party.

SYNONYM: rift; ANTONYM: reconciliation

19. therapeutic (ther ə pyü′ tik)

(*adj.*) having the power to heal or cure; beneficial

Many believe in the ____________________ effects attributed to the waters of natural hot springs.

SYNONYMS: salutary, salubrious
ANTONYMS: harmful, injurious, deleterious

20. virtuoso (vər chü ō′ sō)

(*n.*) a brilliant performer; a person with masterly skill or technique; (*adj.*) masterly or brilliant

Franz Liszt was a piano ____________________.

I was treated to a ____________________ performance.

SYNONYMS: (*n.*) expert, prodigy, maestro
ANTONYMS: (*n.*) amateur, beginner, novice; (*adj.*) mediocre

Choosing the Right Word

*Select the **boldface** word that better completes each sentence. You might refer to the selection on pages 32–33 to see how most of these words are used in context.*

1. In sandpainting, an art still practiced by the Navajos and Pueblos of the American Southwest, designs are created of (**icons, fortes**) representing animals, deities, and natural phenomena.

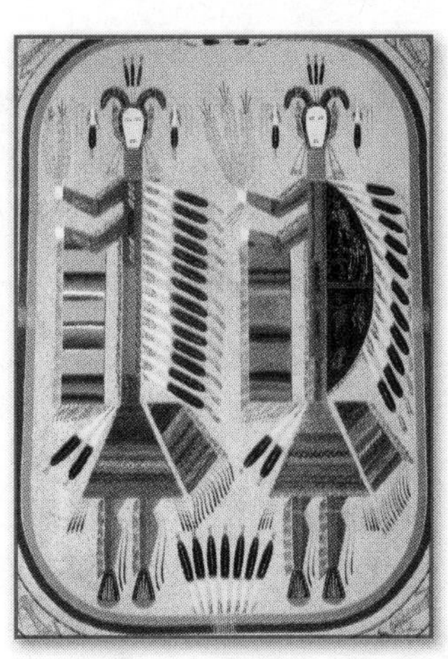

The Navajo call their sandpaintings "places where the gods come and go."

2. Your (**virtuosity, pragmatism**) as an orator may earn you votes, but it cannot make up for your lack of experience in and knowledge of public affairs.

3. We did drop a few objectionable words from the dialogue, but this does not justify the critic's claim that we (**cozened, bowdlerized**) the play.

4. A theory that seems valid in the confines of a small family group may be proved useless when applied in the (**macrocosm, interstice**) of society at large.

5. If you find those people so unpleasant, why do you (**cozen, condescend**) to associate with them?

6. They can't force you to do anything, but it is quite possible that they will be able to (**condescend, cozen**) you into actions against your best interests.

7. The clash of wits between those two brilliant columnists was no mere (**persiflage, paean**), but an exchange of clever insults.

8. The first (**schism, enclave**) in the Communist world of the postwar era occurred in 1948, when Yugoslavia began in earnest to distance itself from the Soviet Union.

9. Our little group of would-be writers, painters, and musicians formed an (**enclave, ancillary**) of culture in what we considered a hostile world.

10. In the great crises of life, you must depend basically on yourself; the help you get from others can only be (**pragmatic, ancillary**).

11. A truly great leader must possess both the inspiration of a visionary and the (**quizzical, pragmatic**) skills of an experienced politician.

12. The sun left its mottled imprint on the wall as the rays filtered through the (**enclaves, interstices**) of the iron grating.

13. In this situation, when I desperately needed material help, I was deluged with a(n) (**plethora, enclave**) of glib and gratuitous advice.

14. A political candidate who promises to solve all our social problems without ever mentioning higher taxes would certainly be dismissed as a (**mountebank, schism**).

15. Because he sees life as a pattern of ambiguities and contradictions, he likes to express himself in the form of (**quizzical, ancillary**) witticisms.

16. The dictum "There's no such thing as a free lunch" means that nothing worthwhile in life comes to us (**forte, gratis**).

17. After the great victory, his quiet and modest statements were far more impressive than the most effusive (**paean, interstice**) could have been.

18. It is a common mistake to assume that shrewdness in business affairs must be accompanied by extreme (**rapacity, mountebank**).

19. Though acupuncture has been practiced in Eastern medicine for centuries, its (**therapeutic, quizzical**) value has only recently been acknowledged in the West.

20. Her easygoing attitude and resilience, far from being weaknesses, proved to be her (**mountebank, forte**) in surviving during that trying period.

21. The introductory membership letter stated that the monthly magazine was delivered (**ancillary, gratis**) but, nonetheless, the membership fees were exorbitant.

22. Many of the celebrated composers of classical pieces were (**icons, virtuosos**) long before they were even teenagers.

23. We exchanged agitated and (**quizzical, pragmatic**) looks after the customs agent instructed us to carry our luggage to a special table for a thorough investigation.

24. A(n) (**macrocosm, icon**) of urban Australia, the Sydney Opera House is a building of unique and masterful construction.

25. The teacher's (**condescending, bowdlerized**) tone inspired many students to drop the course.

Synonyms

*Choose the word from this unit that is the same or most nearly the same in meaning as the **boldface** word or expression in the phrase. Write that word on the line. Use a dictionary if necessary.*

1. **deign** to respond to the question ____________
2. gave their assistance **freely** ____________
3. offered a **hymn** of praise ____________
4. participated in the witty **repartee** ____________
5. urges writers to **censor** their screenplays ____________
6. awed by the gifts of the young **master** ____________
7. the **curative** benefits of mineral water ____________
8. caused a **breach** in their ranks ____________
9. received a **surfeit** of gifts ____________
10. belonging to a **subsidiary** organization ____________

Antonyms

*Choose the word from this unit that is most nearly opposite in meaning to the **boldface** word or expression in the phrase. Write that word on the line. Use a dictionary if necessary.*

1. she acquired the stroller **for a price** ________________
2. the boy's **lament** for his father ________________
3. with a **generosity** heretofore unseen ________________
4. please **append** the volume and add the poem ________________
5. the workers formed a **united front** ________________

Completing the Sentence

From the words in this unit, choose the one that best completes each of the following sentences. Write the word in the space provided.

1. What point is there in dwelling on unproven theories when the problem we are facing demands that we be as ________________ as possible?
2. The coach used diagrams to show our receivers how to slip through the ________________ in our opponent's zone pass coverage.
3. Once the advance and royalties were settled, the publisher and agent negotiated ________________ rights to be covered in the author's contract.
4. My classmates selected me to address the community affairs committee because public speaking is a(n) ________________ of mine.
5. When she neatly faked out the guard, pivoted, and drove in for a layup, I realized that I was seeing a true ________________ on the basketball court.
6. I would have welcomed any firm answer, no matter how unfavorable, but all that I got from her was a(n) ________________ smile.
7. Although we pride ourselves on the advance of civilization, the sad fact is that the ________________ of modern humanity has resulted in more destruction and suffering than ever before in history.
8. At the height of Beatlemania in the mid-1960s the Fab Four assumed the stature of pop ________________ .
9. When the soldiers realized that they had defeated the far more numerous enemy, their cheers rose in a great ________________ of jubilation and victory.
10. A good laugh invariably makes me feel better; I honestly believe that it has a(n) ________________ effect on my disposition.

11. The stubborn old-timers who refused to sell their homes came to form a(n) ____________ of "natives" surrounded by "city people."

12. The situation is growing worse because there is a(n) ____________ of good intentions but a dearth of common sense and willingness to work hard.

13. The "minor difference of opinion" developed into a(n) ____________ that split the political party into two opposing factions.

14. He considers himself such a marvelous chess player that I'm surprised he would ____________ to sit down at the board with a beginner like me.

15. His exaggerated claims for an expensive painkiller that turned out to be no more than aspirin exposed him as a(n) ____________.

16. His self-importance stems from his inability to appreciate the very minor part he plays in the ____________ of human affairs.

17. In attempting to make the novel acceptable to the general public, the editor so ____________ it that it lost its quality of stark realism.

18. She thought of herself as a combination of Mark Twain and H. L. Mencken, but her attempts at "devastating ____________" were not very funny.

19. To promote circulation, the publisher offered to throw in home delivery ____________ for new subscribers to the Sunday edition.

20. Playing on his vanity and his desire to be known as a "good guy," I tried to ____________ him into lending me his car.

Writing: Words in Action

1. Look back at "Charles Ponzi and His Scheme" (pages 32–33). Research a recent, infamous Ponzi scheme. Compare how the more modern scheme is similar to and different from the original Ponzi scheme. Write an essay in which you categorize your findings, using at least three details from the passage and three unit words.

2. *"Do not trouble yourself much to get new things, whether clothes or friends. Turn the old; return to them. Things do not change; we change. Sell your clothes and keep your thoughts."—Henry David Thoreau (Walden)*

   Do you agree with Thoreau's advice? In a brief essay, explain your opinion with specific examples from your studies, reading (refer to pages 32–33), or personal observations and experience. Write at least three paragraphs and use three or more words from this unit.

Vocabulary in Context

Literary Text

*The following excerpts are from novels by Charles Dickens. Some of the words you have studied in this unit appear in **boldface** type. Complete each statement below the excerpt by circling the letter of the correct answer.*

1. When he had looked at it for a long time, he remembered his supper; and resuming the chair he had first occupied, began to eat with great **rapacity**; not like a hungry man, but as if he were determined to do it. He drank too, roundly ... (*Life and Adventures of Martin Chuzzlewit*)

A person who shows **rapacity** is NOT

a. generous　　**c.** joyful
b. emotional　　**d.** skillful

2. This was an antic fellow, half peddler and half **mountebank**, who traveled about the country on foot to vend hones, strops, razors, washballs, harness-paste, medicine for dogs and horses, cheap perfumery, cosmetics, and such-like wares ... (*Oliver Twist*)

A **mountebank** is a(n)

a. salesman　　**c.** swindler
b. actor　　**d.** doctor

3. After swallowing two or three glasses of spirits, Mr. Sikes **condescended** to take some notice of the young gentlemen; which gracious act led to a conversation, in which the cause and manner of Oliver's capture were circumstantially detailed, with such alterations and improvements on the truth, as to the Dodger appeared most advisable under the circumstances. (*Oliver Twist*)

To **condescend** is to

a. entertain others　　**c.** lie to oneself
b. be gracious　　**d.** lower oneself

Smike and Nicholas in the 2002 film adaptation of *Nicholas Nickleby*

4. "He's a treacherous old goat," said Peg, "and **cozened** me with cunning tricks and lying promises, but never mind. I'm even with him. I'm even with him." (*The Life and Adventures of Nicholas Nickleby*)

To **cozen** is to

a. embrace　　**c.** expurgate
b. deceive　　**d.** triumph

5. He assured himself of this, he threw off his clothes, he plunged into the icy water, and swam for the spot. Climbing the timbers, he took from them, caught among their **interstices** by its chain, a gold watch, bearing engraved upon its back E. D. (*The Mystery of Edwin Drood*)

Interstices are

a. intervening spaces　　**c.** branches
b. abundant flora　　**d.** protuberances

Snap the code, or go to **vocabularyworkshop.com**

Vocabulary for Comprehension

*Read the following selection in which some of the words you have studied in Units 1–3 appear in **boldface** type. Then answer the questions on page 43.*

This passage focuses on the life of Winslow Homer, one of America's greatest painters.

(Line)

Winslow Homer's dramatic seascapes continue to fascinate museum visitors and collectors. Born in Boston in 1836, he was just (5) nineteen when his father's importing business soured. Lacking funds for college, he answered an ad and became a lithographer's apprentice. After two years of making bland (10) drawings, he vowed never to be bound to an employer again.

Homer moved to New York to join the city's artistic community. After a mere five art lessons in night school, (15) where he learned the basics of oil painting, he boldly embarked on a career as a freelance illustrator. In 1861, under the **aegis** of *Harper's Weekly*, he attached himself to (20) General George McClellan's Army of the Potomac to draw scenes of Civil War army life in the encampments and near the front lines.

His drawings and sketches (25) showed that he was not a mere realist. His **forte** was his ability to capture the emotional pain and desperation of his subjects, using shape and color to convey his (30) sympathy for the combatants.

Harper's regularly published his unsentimental images of the fear and despair of Civil War soldiers. By the end of the war, Homer was famous.

(35) Not content to be just another **hidebound** artist painting whatever would sell, he traveled to France and, later, to England, where he painted the people of the fishing (40) village of Tynemouth, whose daily lives were affected by their constant struggles with the sea. Returning to America, in a seemingly puzzling move, he settled in Prout's Neck, (45) finding the solitude he needed on the remote and rugged Maine coast. His new paintings depicted the drama of man's heroic battles with the forces of nature.

(50) Except for excursions to Florida and the Caribbean, Homer remained in Maine, far from the celebrity he spurned. Nonetheless, by the late 1880s, he was recognized as (55) America's **virtuoso** seascape painter. Homer died in 1910. This self-taught, fiercely independent artist fully deserves his exalted place in the **hierarchy** of great American painters.

1. The main purpose of the passage is to
   a. analyze Homer's celebrity
   b. analyze Homer's Civil War drawings
   c. highlight the lessons Homer learned on visits to France and England
   d. provide a survey of Homer's career
   e. compare and contrast Homer's Civil War drawings with his seascapes

2. From the passage, you can infer that
   a. Homer's illustrations in *Harper's Weekly* were a popular success
   b. Homer's Civil War drawings and sketches were highly realistic
   c. *Harper's Weekly* favored the North over the South in the Civil War
   d. magazine illustrators were paid very little in Homer's day
   e. more illustrated magazines were published in Boston than in New York

3. The meaning of **aegis** (line 18) is
   a. roof
   b. auspices
   c. scrutiny
   d. employment
   e. discipline

4. Which best identifies the writer's focus in paragraph 3 (lines 24–30)?
   a. the desperation of the combatants
   b. Homer's use of shape and color
   c. Homer's sympathy for his subjects
   d. the importance of realism
   e. Homer's emotional pain

5. **Forte** (line 26) most nearly means
   a. weakness
   b. foible
   c. habit
   d. fortress
   e. strong suit

6. From the passage, you can infer that
   a. Homer's decision to travel to France and England grew from a desire to widen his artistic horizons
   b. Homer was dissatisfied with life in the United States
   c. Homer's fame in England soon equaled his fame in America
   d. Homer found no suitable subjects to paint in England
   e. Homer grew disillusioned with daily life in England

7. **Hidebound** (line 36) is best defined as
   a. enfeebled
   b. unknown
   c. narrow-minded
   d. clothed
   e. flexible

8. Which of the following best describes the organizational structure of the passage?
   a. comparison and contrast
   b. chronological order
   c. cause and effect
   d. spatial order
   e. order of importance

9. **Virtuoso** (line 55) most nearly means
   a. mediocre
   b. leading
   c. amateur
   d. virtuous
   e. masterly

10. **Hierarchy** (line 59) is best defined as
    a. pecking order
    b. court
    c. history
    d. anecdotes
    e. family

11. Which of the following best describes the author's attitude toward the subject?
    a. skeptical
    b. humorous
    c. admiring
    d. neutral
    e. caustic

12. According to the details in the passage, Winslow Homer
    a. had little schooling
    b. was a popular art instructor
    c. never enjoyed recognition as an artist
    d. always had a lot of money
    e. had many children

Two-Word Completions

Select the pair of words that best complete the meaning of each of the following passages.

1. The social structure of the South in the days before the Civil War was rigidly ____________________, with the gentleman planter at the summit of the edifice and the chattel slave at its base. ____________________ notions of caste discouraged whites from moving freely within the system, and the "peculiar institution" denied blacks any mobility whatsoever.

a. pragmatic . . . Polarized
b. hierarchical . . . Hidebound
c. therapeutic . . . Cozened
d. chimerical . . . Obfuscated

2. On more than one occasion during the Middle Ages, controversy about some point of doctrine ____________________ ecclesiastical opinion and produced a temporary ____________________ in the Christian church.

a. polarized . . . schism
b. bowdlerized . . . fait accompli
c. obfuscated . . . enclave
d. deracinated . . . macrocosm

3. As the detachment of knights galloped over the crest of the hill, it collided with a column of enemy foot soldiers moving up the other side. In the brief but bloody ____________________ that ensued, two of the king's most prominent ____________________ lost their lives, and the Duke of Orleans was wounded.

a. schism . . . proselytes
b. purview . . . mountebanks
c. melee . . . vassals
d. vignette . . . bellwethers

4. Your composition is so full of ____________________, malapropisms, and general gobbledygook that I suggest you study a grammar book, a ____________________, and a style manual before you ever again put pen to paper.

a. interstices . . . liturgy
b. raillery . . . microcosm
c. persiflage . . . plethora
d. solecisms . . . lexicon

5. The company's CEO was ____________________ of the dire economic outlook and understood, at once, that he would soon be faced with ____________________ decisions that would either affect executive payrolls or the benefits currently enjoyed by all employees.

a. apprised . . . noisome
b. obfuscated . . . minuscule
c. caterwauled . . . oblivious
d. bowdlerized . . . bibulous

6. At the park, the small child's ____________________, and yet exuberant, facial expressions revealed that the boy was simultaneously intrigued and thrilled by the new playground equipment. In fact, he was positively ____________________ to his mother's entreaties to climb into his stroller and return home.

a. noisome . . . ribald
b. supine . . . chimerical
c. iconic . . . rapacious
d. quizzical . . . oblivious

In the biographical sketch "Fascinating Rhythm: The Life of George Gershwin" (see pages 12–13), the writer notes that one of Gershwin's first hits, performed by Al Jolson, "took the country by storm" and sold more than two million records.

"Take by storm" is an idiom. An **idiom** is a group of words with a meaning different from the literal meanings of each word. For example, "took the country by storm" in the unit opener means that the recorded song was suddenly very successful in the United States. Because the meanings of idioms are sometimes subtle or unexpected, it is important to learn them or look them up in a dictionary.

Choosing the Right Idiom

Read each sentence. Use context clues to figure out the meaning of each idiom in ***boldface*** *print. Then write the letter of the definition for the idiom in the sentence.*

1. Mr. Perez has been entirely **out of commission** since he fractured a bone in his ankle. ______
2. Isn't he a bit too **long in the tooth** to participate in a triathlon? ______
3. The municipality will **come into line** with state and federal governments and will raise taxes. ______
4. **Give** Liz **a wide berth** today—she slept only two hours last night and then lost her cell phone. ______
5. I suspect my father is **in a stew** about the grass that isn't mowed and recycling that isn't sorted. ______
6. As full-time college students, they **live from hand to mouth** and have very few possessions. ______
7. If our costs are **cut to the bone**, we should have enough reserves for an emergency. ______
8. Edwyn **hails from** Wales, but he has been living in the United States for many years now. ______
9. This summer she planted her new garden **by fits and starts**; thus, she will have no yield. ______
10. The investigation had **gotten nowhere fast** and so the police chief decided to hire new detectives. ______

a. conform
b. reduced severely
c. old
d. live on little money
e. unable to function normally
f. comes from originally
g. not made progress
h. upset
i. stay far away from
j. irregularly

Writing with Idioms

Find the meaning of each idiom. (Use an online or print dictionary if necessary.) Then write a sentence for each idiom.

1. lock horns

____

2. upper crust

____

3. doubting Thomas

____

4. no two ways about it

____

5. upset the apple cart

____

____

6. get into hot water

____

____

7. on the heels of something

____

____

8. meat and potatoes

____

9. eat humble pie

____

10. feather one's own nest

____

11. cast around for

____

12. bury one's head in the sand

____

Denotation and Connotation

The literal meaning of a word is its **denotation**. This meaning is found in a dictionary. A word also has a **connotation**, or an implied meaning, that readers or listeners attribute to it. These informal meanings are sometimes a result of personal associations. Many words have connotations that are either *positive* or *negative*.

For example, a writer could describe a character's intellectual capabilities in any of the following ways: *brainy, clever, know-it-all, brilliant, wise, experienced,* and so on. Each of these words conveys different images or ideas in a reader's mind. Writers intentionally choose a particular word in order to best express a precise mood or message. Consider these synonyms for the negative word *oblivious*:

unsuspecting *unwitting* *unaware* *clueless*

Unsuspecting and *unwitting* have positive connotations, suggesting someone who isn't suspicious, and *unaware* is typically used as a neutral word. *Clueless* may have a negative connotation, suggesting carelessness.

Think: A small child may be unsuspecting of an older child trying to trick him, but a young man speaking loudly on his cell phone in a movie theater may be oblivious or clueless.

Look at these examples of words that are similar in denotation but have different connotations.

NEUTRAL	POSITIVE	NEGATIVE
fans	**devotees**	**claque**
apprise	**enlighten**	**lecture**
conservative	**traditional**	**hidebound**

Both writers and readers benefit from understanding the powerful and subjective meanings that certain words may have. While writing and reading, it is important to pay attention to the nuances of connotation.

Shades of Meaning

Write a plus sign (+) in the box if the word has a positive connotation. Write a minus sign (–) if the word has a negative connotation. Put a zero (0) if the word is neutral.

1. caterwaul ☐ **2.** adjunct ☐ **3.** vignette ☐ **4.** morass ☐

5. mountebank ☐ **6.** therapeutic ☐ **7.** virtuoso ☐ **8.** condescend ☐

9. cozen ☐ **10.** ancillary ☐ **11.** forte ☐ **12.** poltroon ☐

13. versimilitude ☐ **14.** noisome ☐ **15.** effete ☐ **16.** sanguine ☐

Expressing the Connotation

Read each sentence. Select the word in parentheses that expresses the connotation (positive, negative, or neutral) given at the beginning of the sentence.

negative	**1.** In the (**crowd, melee**), I lost sight of my friends and then became entirely disoriented.
neutral	**2.** For the artist, painting was (**marginal, ancillary**) to the great love of her life, sculpting.
negative	**3.** As one motorist recounted his point of view, the other driver's (**derision, persiflage**) became unbearable.
neutral	**4.** The (**vassal, secondary**) status of the city council ensured that the mayor had the majority of local power.
positive	**5.** You have made a (**pragmatic, hardheaded**) decision of which, with reflection, you can be proud.
neutral	**6.** The hypothesis that Earth revolves around the Sun (**alienated, polarized**) people in Renaissance times.
negative	**7.** The (**lachrymose, emotional**) account of the heroic Dalmatian was poorly written and manipulative.
positive	**8.** The (**compact, minuscule**) and well-appointed quarters were efficiently designed—and even cozy.

Challenge: Using Connotation

Choose vocabulary words from Units 1–3 to replace the highlighted words in the sentences below. Then explain how the connotation of the replacement word changes the tone of the sentence.

melee	**bibulous**	**bellwether**
ribald	**raillery**	**proselyte**

1. Lucia was accustomed to enduring **ridicule** ____________________ in the school lunchroom after changing her hair color.

____

2. After the game's umpire announced her decision, the opposing teams exchanged insults—and then the **disruption** ____________________ commenced.

____

3. It was reported that after his acceptance speech, the mayor told a **crude** ____________________ anecdote to his entourage—and also to the eavesdropping journalists.

____

Classical Roots

sem, simil, simul—like; together; at the same time

This root appears in **verisimilitude** (page 26), which means "the appearance of being true." Some other words based on the same root are listed below.

assemblage	**disassemble**	**simile**	**simulation**
assimilation	**resemblance**	**simulacrum**	**simulcast**

From the list of words above, choose the one that corresponds to each of the brief definitions below. Write the word in the blank space in the illustrative sentence below the definition. Use an online or print dictionary if necessary.

1. a collection of people or things; a gathering

The most experienced journalists were sent to cover the annual ____________________ of notables in the field of medical research.

2. a similarity in form or appearance; a likeness

Grandma glows over the strong family ____________________ she already sees in her newborn grandson.

3. to take apart

After the science fair, it took the exhibitors and maintenance crew several hours to fully ____________________ the many displays and booths.

4. an image or representation of something; an unreal or superficial semblance

The first 1950s television sitcoms presented a cheery ____________________ of family happiness.

5. to broadcast over radio and television at the same time

She had some friends over to enjoy the ____________________ of the rock concert with her.

6. the act or process of taking on the appearance or form of something; a feigning or pretending

Although the children were unable to keep the secret from their mother, she put on a convincing ____________________ of surprise at the presentation of their gift.

7. a comparison, introduced by *like* or *as*; an analogy

A nonfiction essay on a dreary topic can be enlivened by poetic use of ____________________.

8. the act or process of taking in or absorbing; the state of being absorbed

The healthy human brain is uniquely designed for constant ____________________ of knowledge.

Read the following selection, taking note of the ***boldface*** *words and their contexts. These words are among those you will be studying in Unit 4. As you complete the exercises in this unit, it may help to refer to the way the words are used below.*

Putting Social Media in Perspective

<Speech>

Rhiannon Marsh, Washington, DC, November 1, 2012

Distinguished guests and fellow media enthusiasts, I am honored to speak with you today at this first-ever Modern Media Forum.

When the Philippine Congress voted to ignore evidence that threatened to secure the impeachment of the Philippine president in 2001, angry Filipinos poured into the streets to protest. That protest was arranged, in part, by text messages exchanged among ordinary citizens, perhaps a million of whom gathered in the capital. In response to the demonstration, the Congress immediately performed a **volte-face**, deciding to put the crucial evidence in play, and the president was forced to resign.

When Ukrainian elections were tainted by suspicions of fraud in 2004, pro-democracy activists in that country went online. The **obloquies** they posted on internet forums publicized their leaders' **bilious** corruption, helping to spread the word and rouse the **hoi polloi**. With the movement gathering steam, activists and angry citizens used internet forums and text messages to coordinate mass protests. As a result of these protests, a revote was called and a new president was elected.

Above: Filipinos celebrate their new president after street protests led to the ouster of Joseph Estrada.

Left: Benjamin Franklin operates a printing press.

Increasingly, protesters around the world employ the whole **gamut** of social media tools, including microblogging, social networking, and video-sharing sites, to spread news and organize action. Political **pundits**, excited by the trend, have rushed to declare that social media tools are ushering in a new era of revolution against

Above: Ukrainians celebrate the first anniversary of the Orange Revolution street protests that led to a change of president.

Below: A protest in Tahrir Square, Cairo

oppressive regimes. What should we make of these pundits' **divinations**? Do social media really give the world's masses an unprecedented potential to effect political change, or is the excitement about social media's role in twenty-first-century protests merely a **corollary** of the **pundits' affinity** for exaggeration?

No great **lucubration** is required to answer the question. While the technology employed by protesters today is **symptomatic** of our times, the basic **parameters** that cause mass protests, and that determine their success or failure, remain unchanged. The printing press was employed by activists of the American Revolution. Fax machines helped direct the revolutions in Eastern Europe in 1989. Where there's a will, there's a way. When corruption, oppression, and a dearth of economic opportunity combine to wake the **ineffable** spirit of protest in a nation, the people use whatever means are available to express their discontent. When a people rise up to demand democracy, it is the fact of their courage in the face of oppression that deserves our attention, their feats of **derring-do** both great and small, the purpose of their movement, its causes and its course. What tools they use is an inessential matter, an accident of history. Political commentators' obsession with the role of social media in the popular movements of our new century would be **risible**, were it not for the fact that the noise they make distracts our public discourse from more important themes. In recent months, as millions throughout the Arab world have taken to the streets to shout down their oppressors and demand democracy, too much American ink has been spilled commenting on the protesters' use of cell phones and social networking utilities.

To be fair, not every remark on the subject deserves to be treated as **folderol.** Social media's greatest impact is that they enable ordinary citizens to reach wide audiences instantly. These tools are democratizing communication, putting the power of publication in the hands of the many. But while this welcome trend is noteworthy, we should not let it distract us from the subject that most deserves our attention: the spread of democracy itself.

Snap the code, or go to **vocabularyworkshop.com**

Note the spelling, pronunciation, part(s) of speech, and definition(s) of each of the following words. Then write the word in the blank spaces in the illustrative sentence(s) following. Finally, study the lists of synonyms and antonyms.

1. affinity
(ə fin′ ə te)

(*n.*) a natural attraction to a person, thing, or activity; a relationship, connection

The mysterious _______________ between the two leaders could not be explained.

SYNONYMS: inclination, penchant; ANTONYMS: aversion, distaste

2. bilious
(bil′ yəs)

(*adj.*) peevish or irritable; sickeningly unpleasant

The room was painted a _______________ shade of green.

SYNONYMS: choleric, irascible, peevish, splenetic
ANTONYMS: sweet-tempered, genial, pleasant, delightful

3. cognate
(kog′ nāt)

(*adj.*) closely related in origin, essential nature, or function; (*n.*) such a person or thing

_______________ languages, such as Spanish, Italian, and French, share a common root.

When I studied Latin, I learned that the words *pater* and *father* are _______________.

SYNONYMS: (*adj.*) allied, affiliated; (*n.*) relative
ANTONYM: (*adj.*) dissimilar

4. corollary
(kôr′ ə ler ē)

(*n.*) a proposition that follows from one already proven; a natural consequence or result; (*adj.*) resultant or consequent

Learning the axiom and its _______________ was no simple matter.

The _______________ effects of today's findings remain to be seen.

SYNONYMS: (*n.*) deduction, conclusion
ANTONYMS: (*n.*) axiom, postulate, premise

5. cul-de-sac
(kəl′ də sak)

(*n.*) a blind alley or dead-end street; any situation in which further progress is impossible; an impasse

Much to their dismay, the once-optimistic negotiators found themselves in a hopeless _______________.

6. derring-do
(der′ iŋ dü)

(*n.*) valor or heroism; daring deeds or exploits (often used to poke fun at false heroics)

Breathtaking feats of _______________ are all in a day's work for a Hollywood stuntperson.

SYNONYMS: audacity, bravado, pyrotechnics
ANTONYMS: cowardice, poltroonery

7. divination (div ə nā′ shən)

(*n.*) the art or act of predicting the future or discovering hidden knowledge

Claiming skill in ____________________, the fortune teller took my money and then told me what my future held.

SYNONYM: prophecy

8. elixir (i lik′ sər)

(*n.*) a potion once thought capable of curing all ills and maintaining life indefinitely; a panacea; a sweet liquid used as a vehicle in medicines

Allegedly, the explorer Ponce de León spent years searching for the ____________________ of eternal life.

SYNONYMS: nostrum, tonic

9. folderol (fol′ də rol)

(*n.*) foolish talk, ideas, or procedures; nonsense; a trifle

Right from the outset, the sergeant informed her troops that she would not tolerate any ____________________.

SYNONYM: gibberish

ANTONYMS: sense, significance

10. gamut (gam′ ət)

(*n.*) an entire range or series

The reviews of the newest Broadway musical extravaganza ran the ____________________ from praise to scorn.

SYNONYMS: compass, sweep

11. hoi polloi (hoi pə loi′)

(*n.*) the common people, the masses

By catering to the ____________________, the studio was able to make one very successful movie after another.

SYNONYM: rank and file

ANTONYMS: aristocracy, elite, upper class

12. ineffable (in ef′ ə bəl)

(*adj.*) not expressible in words; too great or too sacred to be uttered

The ____________________ joy of parenthood is the subject of a psychologist's new bestseller.

SYNONYM: inexpressible

13. lucubration (lü ky brā′ shən)

(*n.*) laborious study or thought, especially at night; the result of such work

The scientist's ____________________ took place after midnight, secretly, in the quiet of the laboratory.

SYNONYM: burning the midnight oil

14. mnemonic (ni mon′ ik)

(*adj.*) relating to or designed to assist the memory; (*n.*) a device to aid the memory

"Please Excuse My Dear Aunt Sally" is a ____________________ device used to remember the order of mathematical operations.

The ____________________ HOMES can help people to recall the names of the Great Lakes.

SYNONYMS: (*n.*) reminder, cue

15. obloquy (ob′ lə kwē)

(*n.*) public abuse indicating strong disapproval or censure; the disgrace resulting from such treatment

The press heaped ____________________ on the head of the offending official.

SYNONYMS: discredit, opprobrium, dishonor
ANTONYMS: praise, acclaim, approbation

16. parameter (pə ram′ ə tər)

(*n.*) a determining or characteristic element; a factor that shapes the total outcome; a limit, boundary

The committee analyzed the ____________________ of the nation's military potential.

17. pundit (pən′ dit)

(*n.*) a learned person; one who gives authoritative opinions

A renowned ____________________ of the theater, the critic had the power to affect a show's success.

SYNONYMS: expert, authority, savant
ANTONYMS: dilettante, layman, amateur

18. risible (riz′ ə bəl)

(*adj.*) pertaining to laughter; able or inclined to laugh; laughable

All in the crowd, not just the children, were delighted by the ____________________ antics of the clowns.

SYNONYMS: droll, ludicrous
ANTONYMS: depressing, heartrending, poignant

19. symptomatic (simp tə mat′ ik)

(*adj.*) typical or characteristic; being or concerned with a symptom of a disease

According to certain sociologists, vulgarity and indulgence are ____________________ of a nation's decline.

SYNONYM: indicative

20. volte-face (volt fäs′)

(*n.*) an about-face; a complete reversal

The prosecution's witness's testimony amounted to a completely unexpected ____________________.

SYNONYM: turnabout

Choosing the Right Word

*Select the **boldface** word that better completes each sentence. You might refer to the selection on pages 50–51 to see how most of these words are used in context.*

1. The devastating stock market crash of 1929 surprised not only laymen, but Wall Street (**corollaries, pundits**) as well.

2. It may seem to be a paradox, but I believe it is true that only a basically serious person can fully appreciate the (**risible, bilious**) factors in life.

3. You have had many difficulties in life, but you are helping no one by behaving in such a (**bilious, cognate**) manner.

4. No student of anthropology can fail to recognize the (**cognate, corollary**) elements in the cultures of societies which seem to be vastly different from one another.

The stock market crashed on Black Tuesday in October 1929 and once-wealthy people found themselves trying to raise cash. This man is selling his new car for $100.

5. The advice that they offered us with such pretentious solemnity turned out to be nothing more than platitudes and (**folderol, elixir**).

6. We found it more difficult to master the (**mnemonic, parameter**) than it would have been to memorize the material to which it was keyed.

7. Only a supreme actor could express so eloquently the (**risible, ineffable**) quality of the "thoughts that do often lie too deep for tears."

8. Is your repeated use of the expression (**cul-de-sac, hoi polloi**) supposed to convey the idea that you are not one of the people?

9. I knew that if I ran for public office, I would be exposed to severe criticism, but I never expected such a flood of (**obloquy, elixir**).

10. Henry had an excellent chance to make an honorable career for himself, but he seemed to have a fatal (**affinity, corollary**) for easy money and shady deals.

11. Those remarkably accurate predictions were based not on (**derring-do, divination**) but on insight into human nature and the objective elements in the situation.

12. In the *Inferno*, Dante introduces personages from history and mythology to portray the full (**gamut, folderol**) of human folly and wickedness.

13. Many sociologists believe that the high divorce rate in the United States is (**symptomatic, ineffable**) of basic strains and flaws in our social structure.

14. Your irresponsible behavior has finally caught up with you; you are in a (**cul-de-sac, hoi polloi**) from which it will be all but impossible to extricate yourself.

15. It is little short of incredible that all their copious (**lucubrations, divinations**) have brought forth that tiny mouse of an idea.

16. I have listened to them state that the present situation is hopeless, but I am unwilling to accept the (**gamut, corollary**) that the only course open to us is surrender.

17. We expect to see politicians modify their points of view from time to time, but a sudden, unexpected (**cognate, volte-face**) by a candidate is more than we can tolerate.

18. In an age of genocide, atomic weapons, and threats of ecological disaster, do you really expect a sensible person to be fascinated by such romantic tales of (**parameters, derring-do**)?

19. The pithy comments of that brilliant and delightful woman were a(n) (**elixir, cul-de-sac**) that we found extraordinarily exhilarating.

20. The first thing we must do is establish the (**parameters, lucubrations**) of the problem, so that we can begin to think in terms of a practical solution.

21. The study of (**elixirs, cognates**) helped me perform well in the vocabulary portion of the standardized test because many English words are related to Greek and Latin words.

22. It was a test of endurance, to be polite, to pour through the scholar's (**pundits, lucubrations**) on the origin of the maypole.

23. Somehow the athlete prevailed over the (**obloquy, gamut**) resulting from the highly publicized—and emotionally charged—trial of her family member.

24. During the epidemic, a great majority of the wards were designated for the (**symptomatic, risible**) patients who might transmit the disease to the general population.

25. The (**mnemonic, corollary**) effect of the oil spill was a decline in fish population.

Synonyms

Choose the word from this unit that is the same or most nearly the same in meaning as the ***boldface*** *word or expression in the phrase. Write that word on the line. Use a dictionary if necessary.*

1. the **augury** of the oracle ____________
2. among the **related** procedures ____________
3. suffered a torrent of **ignominy** ____________
4. the **indescribable** beauty of the canyons ____________
5. wondered what all the **hoopla** was about ____________
6. not the **cure-all** the mountebank promised ____________
7. led the despondent explorers to a **dead end** ____________
8. spent the late hours in **deep thought** ____________
9. the **scope** of the case before the judge ____________
10. a **memory aid** for recalling the rainbow's colors ____________

Antonyms

*Choose the word from this unit that is most nearly opposite in meaning to the **boldface** word or expression in the phrase. Write that word on the line. Use a dictionary if necessary.*

1. the powder was a **poison** to the rats ____________________
2. was not the time for **timidity** ____________________
3. poor study habits are a certain **way to forget** ____________________
4. the **thoroughfare** leads to a bridge across the river ____________________
5. the words *door* and *dour* are **unrelated words** ____________________

Completing the Sentence

From the words in this unit, choose the one that best completes each of the following sentences. Write the word in the space provided.

1. The suggestion was so ____________________ that I couldn't help laughing out loud as soon as I heard it.
2. The intensive merchandising and tremendous sale of patent medicines show that mankind has never really ceased its search for an all-purpose ____________________.
3. Foreign visitors sometimes dismiss our national political conventions as mere ____________________ because of all the surface pageantry.
4. All kittens display a natural ____________________ for mischief, but I have never known one so bent on monkey business as our Mickie.
5. The role calls for an actor who can express a(n) ____________________ of emotions, from speechless rage to utter bliss.
6. After having strongly supported the teaching of foreign languages, they made a complete ____________________ and advocated that this part of the curriculum be dropped or limited to a small minority.
7. In reading a passage in French, I can often guess the meanings of words I have never seen before because they are recognizable ____________________ of familiar English words.
8. The ____________________ tenor of the remarks that they offered to us as "constructive criticism" betrayed just how sorely they envied our success.
9. In estimating the relative military strength of the two powers, we must concentrate on the ____________________ by which ability to carry on modern warfare may be judged.
10. The lecturer said that the soaring crime statistics are ____________________ of a society in which traditional values and standards are breaking down.

11. This short sentence will serve as a(n) ____________________ to help you remember the names of the first eight Presidents: "*W*ill *A* *J*olly *M*an *M*ake *A* *J*olly *V*isitor?"

12. I know that they deserve to be condemned, but I can't bring myself to heap ____________________ on them when they are in such a state of disgrace.

13. In a truly democratic society, there are no sharp differences in status and privilege between self-styled aristocrats and the ____________________.

14. The situation calls for courage, in the sense of a sustained, resolute, and patient effort—not occasional feats of ____________________.

15. The relief we felt when we realized they were safe was so profound and overwhelming as to be utterly ____________________.

16. Is our blind faith in computerized analysis any different in its essentials from the belief of so-called primitive peoples in ____________________?

17. Having been maneuvered into a(n) ____________________, the retreating troops could do nothing but turn and fight a battle for survival against superior forces.

18. No sooner did the press conference end than the network correspondent turned to a group of political ____________________ for an instant analysis.

19. Your ponderous ____________________ seemed to me intended much more to emphasize your own importance than to shed any real light on the subject.

20. It is true that capital punishment has not been proved to be a deterrent to murder, but it would be invalid to draw from this the ____________________ that it has been proved *not* to be a deterrent.

Writing: Words in Action

1. Look back at "Putting Social Media in Perspective" (pages 50–51). Consider the causes and effects of some of the great social and political revolutions of the twentieth and twenty-first centuries. Write a cause-and-effect essay that describes some causes of these major uprisings and collective public action, using at least three details from the passage and three unit words.

2. *"There is a limit to the legitimate interference of collective opinion with individual independence: and to find that limit, and maintain it against encroachment, is as indispensable to a good condition of human affairs, as protection against political despotism."—John Stuart Mill*

   Do you agree with Mill's statement? In a brief essay, explain your opinion with specific examples from your studies, reading (refer to pages 50–51), or personal observations and experience. Write at least three paragraphs, and use three or more words from this unit.

Vocabulary in Context

Literary Text

The following excerpts are from Henry Fielding's novels The History of Tom Jones, Amelia, *and* Joseph Andrews. *Some of the words you have studied in this unit appear in* **boldface** *type. Complete each statement below the excerpt by circling the letter of the correct answer.*

1. "He never wanted rest less than at present; for that day and night were indifferent seasons to him; and that he commonly made use of the former for the time of his repose and of the latter for his walks and **lucubrations**." (*The History of Tom Jones*)

Lucubrations are

a. memories	**c.** conversations
b. meditations	**d.** folderols

2. He therefore dismissed her with assurances that he would very soon remove her out of the reach of that **obloquy** she had incurred; concluding with some additional documents, in which he recommended repentance .... (*The History of Tom Jones*)

Someone who faces **obloquy** faces

a. oblivion	**c.** criticism
b. negotiation	**d.** equanimity

3. "Can such a man reflect that he hath the **ineffable** honor to be employed in the immediate service of his great Creator? Or can he please himself with the heart-warming hope that his ways are acceptable in the sight of that glorious, that incomprehensible Being?" (*Amelia*)

Something **ineffable** is also

a. unutterable	**c.** common
b. coincidental	**d.** medicinal

Albert Finney stars in the Academy Award-winning *Tom Jones*.

4. He was handsome ... and yet ... he made so awkward an appearance in Mrs. Ellison's parlor, that the good lady herself, who had invited him in, could at first scarce refrain from laughter at his behavior. He had not, however, been long in the room before admiration of his person got the better of such **risible** ideas. (*Amelia*)

Risible ideas are NOT

a. frivolous	**c.** ridiculous
b. fraught	**d.** solemn

5. "He feared he was; for that his pulse was very exalted and feverish, and, if his fever should prove more than **symptomatic**, it would be impossible to save him." (*Joseph Andrews, Volume I*)

When something is **symptomatic**, it is a

a. trifle	**c.** dread
b. passion	**d.** sign

Snap the code, or go to **vocabularyworkshop.com**

*Read the following selection, taking note of the **boldface** words and their contexts. These words are among those you will be studying in Unit 5. As you complete the exercises in this unit, it may help to refer to the way the words are used below.*

The Comics and Cartoons of Winsor McCay

<Informational Essay>

A century ago, it was not uncommon for Americans, young and old, to spend Sunday afternoons with the comic strips spread out before them in a newspaper. For a nickel, the **insouciant** reader could relax and enjoy the antics of cartoon heroes like the Katzenjammer Kids, Mr. Jack, Happy Hooligan, and Buster Brown. Some early comic strips expressed **tendentious** political opinions; some were, like **homilies**, aimed at shaping the character of their audiences; but almost all of them aimed to get a guffaw out of their readers by means of simple, slapstick humor. One comic strip, however, stood out from the turn-of-the-century **matrix** of high jinks and monkeyshines. *Little Nemo in Slumberland,* by Winsor McCay, was subtle, surreal, and sometimes downright creepy.

Winsor McCay creating storyboards

As a teenager, McCay's parents **browbeat** him into attending business school in Michigan, but the young man felt **immured** by the school, and refused to be corralled into the way of life it represented. What he really wanted to do was draw—he'd been drawing since childhood, and over time his art had become something **sacrosanct** to him. It started to help him earn a living, too. He found work at a dime museum in Detroit, drawing portraits of visitors, for which he received an **emolument** of 25¢ apiece—fair compensation at a time when the average American worker earned about $400 per year.

In 1903, McCay landed a job creating cartoon strips for the *New York Herald.* His masterpiece, *Little Nemo in Slumberland*, debuted two years later. The hero of the strip, a boy named Nemo, had a new dream adventure each week, often barely avoiding disaster in his ongoing attempt to get to Slumberland, the domain of King Morpheus. McCay used inspired graphic experimentation and brilliant colors to present these fantasy sequences with unprecedented **panache**, and in so doing, he revolutionized the comic strip **genre** and influenced generations of cartoonists to come.

McCay made a brilliant **foray** into animated cartoons and in 1914, created the beautiful short film *Gertie the Dinosaur.* Gertie is widely considered to be the first cartoon character created especially for film that had a developed **persona**. While *Little Nemo* had been celebrated among **aficionados** more than it was adored by the average comic strip reader, *Gertie's* popular success was **commensurate** with the critical acclaim it received. By today's standards the film is short and remarkably simple. But in its day, *Gertie* was another landmark achievement for its creator, captivating audiences and cementing McCay's reputation as a pioneering master of his craft who stood head and shoulders above the other cartoonists of his day.

Comics and animated cartoons have evolved in the decades since McCay created his most memorable works, and they continue to evolve today. Artistic techniques keep pace with **systemic** changes in the technologies of print and film; content, styles, and themes vary along with the **vicissitudes** of modern culture. But McCay's influence—acknowledged by subsequent legends from Walt Disney to Chuck Jones, from Walter Lantz to Maurice Sendak—is one of the enduring features of the art.

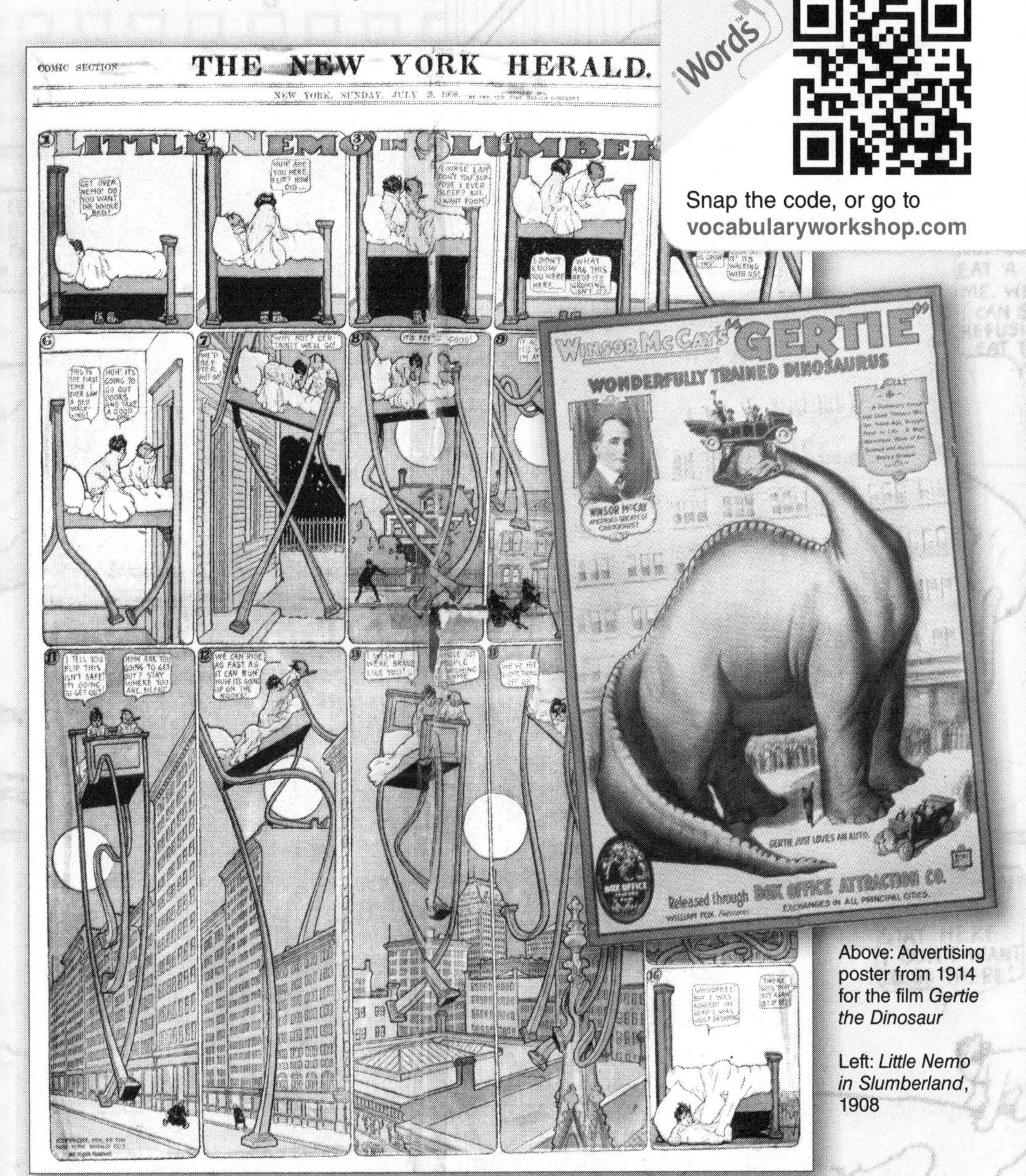

Above: Advertising poster from 1914 for the film *Gertie the Dinosaur*

Left: *Little Nemo in Slumberland*, 1908

Note the spelling, pronunciation, part(s) of speech, and definition(s) of each of the following words. Then write the word in the blank spaces in the illustrative sentence(s) following. Finally, study the lists of synonyms and antonyms.

1. aficionado
(ə fish yə nä′ dō)

(*n.*) an enthusiastic and usually expert follower or fan

I have been an ____________ of football since my youth.

SYNONYMS: devotee, enthusiast

2. browbeat
(braů′ bēt)

(*v.*) to intimidate by a stern or overbearing manner; to bully

The dissatisfied customer had to ____________ the store manager into refunding his money.

SYNONYMS: cow, coerce
ANTONYMS: cajole, coax, wheedle, sweet-talk

3. commensurate
(kə men′ sə rit)

(*adj.*) equal in size, extent, duration, or importance; proportionate; measurable by the same standards

All employees got raises ____________ with their efforts.

SYNONYMS: comparable, corresponding, coordinate

4. diaphanous
(dī af′ ə nəs)

(*adj.*) very sheer and light; almost completely transparent

We were asked to use a ____________ material like gauze to make the costumes.

SYNONYMS: translucent, gossamer
ANTONYMS: opaque, dense

5. emolument
(i mol′ yə mənt)

(*n.*) profit derived from an office or position or from employment; a fee or salary

Choosing an equitable ____________ for the mayor was the latest of the city council's acts.

SYNONYMS: pay, wages

6. foray
(fôr′ ā)

(*n.*) a quick raid, especially for plunder; a venture into some field of endeavor; (*v.*) to make such a raid

The cavalry's ____________ behind enemy lines was a great success.

Counting on the element of surprise, the general ordered the troops to begin to ____________ before dawn.

SYNONYMS: (*n.*) sally, sortie
ANTONYM: (*n.*) retreat

7. genre
(zhän′ rə)

(*n.*) a type, class, or variety, especially a distinctive category of literary composition; a style of painting in which everyday scenes are realistically depicted

The science fiction ____________ has produced several classics.

SYNONYMS: species, sort, school

8. homily
(hom′ ə lē)

(*n.*) a sermon stressing moral principles; a tedious moralizing lecture or discourse

The topic of this week's ____________ is respect for diversity.

9. immure
(i myůr′)

(*v.*) to enclose or confine within walls; to imprison; to seclude or isolate

The criminal was ____________ for life in a narrow cell.

SYNONYM: mew up
ANTONYMS: release, liberate, emancipate

10. insouciant
(in sü′ sē ənt)

(*adj.*) blithely indifferent or unconcerned; carefree; happy-go-lucky

After months of worrying about the fate of his new project, the man was determined to lead a more ____________ life thereafter.

SYNONYMS: blasé, devil-may-care
ANTONYMS: worried, careworn, agitated, distraught

11. matrix
(mā′ triks)

(*n.*) a mold; the surrounding situation or environment

Scientists discovered a tiny prehistoric creature fossilized in a ____________ of amber.

SYNONYMS: pattern, model

12. obsequies
(ob′ sə kwēz)

(*n.*) funeral rites or ceremonies

The nation held somber ____________ for its beloved leader.

SYNONYM: funeral services

13. panache
(pə nash′)

(*n.*) a confident and stylish manner, dash; a strikingly elaborate or colorful display

In the film *The Adventures of Robin Hood*, the actor Errol Flynn captures the ____________ of the bandit.

SYNONYMS: style, verve, élan, éclat

14. persona
(pər sō′ nə)

(*n.*) a character in a novel or play; the outward character or role that a person assumes

The comic ________________ of Charlie Chaplin is recognizable the world over.

SYNONYMS: personality, image, role

15. philippic
(fi lip′ ik)

(*n.*) a bitter verbal attack

The senator delivered a ________________ against the proposed law and those who supported it.

SYNONYMS: harangue, diatribe
ANTONYMS: encomium, panegyric

16. prurient
(pru̇ r′ ē ənt)

(*adj.*) having lustful desires or interests; tending to arouse sexual desires

Considered a ________________ novel by some, *Ulysses* was once banned from sale in the United States.

SYNONYMS: lascivious, lewd, titillating
ANTONYMS: prudish, demure

17. sacrosanct
(sak′ rō saŋkt)

(*adj.*) very sacred or holy; inviolable; set apart or immune from questioning or attack

Members of the clergy felt privileged to be entrusted with guarding the ________________ relic.

18. systemic
(sis tem′ ik)

(*adj.*) of or pertaining to the entire body; relating to a system or systems

The singer suffered a ________________ breakdown after the long and demanding season.

SYNONYMS: extensive, comprehensive, system-wide
ANTONYMS: specific, isolated, confined, localized

19. tendentious
(ten den′ shəs)

(*adj.*) intended to promote a particular point of view, doctrine, or cause; biased or partisan

The candidate's supporters heartily applauded her ________________ arguments.

SYNONYM: partial
ANTONYMS: fair, equitable, disinterested

20. vicissitude
(vi sis′ ə tüd)

(*n.*) a change, variation, or alteration; (*pl.*) successive or changing phases or conditions

The inevitable ________________ of life affect us all.

SYNONYMS: fluctuation, vacillation
ANTONYMS: sameness, evenness

Choosing the Right Word

*Select the **boldface** word that better completes each sentence. You might refer to the selection on pages 60–61 to see how most of these words are used in context.*

1. It is often said that in Russia there are as many (**vicissitudes, aficionados**) of chess as there are of baseball or golf in the United States.

2. If the woman thinks her status as a public official renders her (**insouciant, sacrosanct**), she is in for a rude awakening.

3. Common sense reminds us that even in moments of great joy we should retain some awareness of the (**panache, vicissitudes**) and heartbreaks of life.

4. What we owe to our fallen leader is not mournful (**philippics, obsequies**) but a joyful assertion of life and a pledge to continue her work.

5. I admit that you have some grounds for complaint, but those shrieks of outrage are simply not (**diaphanous, commensurate**) with having been overcharged five cents.

The Russian Garry Kasparov became the World Chess Champion in 1985, at age 22.

6. It seems incredible that a few generations ago a novel of such quality could be widely condemned as designed to appeal to (**tendentious, prurient**) interests.

7. The fact that they referred to my salary as a(n) (**panache, emolument**) did not disguise the fact that I was being woefully underpaid.

8. How can young people hope to become mature, self-reliant adults if they (**immure, foray**) themselves in a home environment that is overly comfortable and protective?

9. I had hoped to hear a balanced, dispassionate discussion of this problem, but I found their approach to be distressingly one-sided and (**tendentious, sacrosanct**).

10. There is no doubt of your oratorical talents, but this is a time for quiet words of reconciliation—not for thundering (**emoluments, philippics**).

11. The purpose of our policies is to develop bold forms of international understanding and practical cooperation that can serve as the (**philippic, matrix**) for peace.

12. The commission found that police corruption was not confined to one or two isolated precincts but was (**systemic, prurient**) in nature.

13. James Bond seems to dispose of the villains he faces with all the (**genre, panache**) of the legendary paladins of medieval romance.

14. People involved in drug abuse need practical help in overcoming their addiction—not (**homilies, obsequies**) exhorting them to higher standards of behavior.

15. The defense attorney claimed that the police had used scare tactics to (**browbeat, foray**) her client into a confession.

16. Corot painted poetic and (**diaphanous, tendentious**) landscapes, in which even solid objects seemed to be suffused with light and movement.

17. Certainly your judgment, if not your motives, must be questioned when you choose to associate yourself with an organization of that (**matrix, genre**).

18. The (**matrix, persona**) that a public figure displays to the world is often quite different from the personality that he or she exhibits in private.

19. What gourmet feast can compare with the luscious delicacies that we consumed during our midnight (**forays, homilies**) on the well-stocked refrigerator?

20. When the results of the scholarship competition were announced, we could sense the deep disappointment beneath your (**insouciant, tendentious**) manner.

21. The writing instructor requested that we not (**immure, foray**) into poetry until we learn how to master the art of prose.

22. The majority of patients experienced (**tendentious, systemic**) symptoms such as fever, extreme weight loss, and night sweats.

23. The Flemish painter Pieter Brueghel the Elder is known for his magnificent (**genre, panache**) scenes in which peasants are portrayed in their quotidian activities.

24. After a hurricane completely ravaged their city, the minister's (**homily, emolument**) seemed pedantic and heartless.

25. To portray the (**vicissitude, persona**) of Falstaff, a performer must possess instinctive comic timing.

Choose the word from this unit that is the same or most nearly the same in meaning as the ***boldface*** *word or expression in the phrase. Write that word on the line. Use a dictionary if necessary.*

1. **compensation** for the job ____________
2. the **see-through** curtain glowed as night fell ____________
3. envied their **nonchalant** approach ____________
4. was seen as **salacious** behavior ____________
5. **incarcerated** in a dungeon ____________
6. possessed a certain **flamboyance** ____________
7. considered to be a **sacred** duty ____________
8. pay **proportionate** to the task ____________
9. let loose a searing **tirade** ____________
10. delivered the **last rites** ____________

Antonyms

*Choose the word from this unit that is most nearly opposite in meaning to the **boldface** word or expression in the phrase. Write that word on the line. Use a dictionary if necessary.*

1. made of **coarse** material ____________________
2. stunned by their **impartial** response ____________________
3. **innocent** gazes across the dance floor ____________________
4. **birth celebrations** in honor of the new prince ____________________
5. a **tribute** delivered to memorialize fallen soldiers ____________________

Completing the Sentence

From the words in this unit, choose the one that best completes each of the following sentences. Write the word in the space provided.

1. When doctors discovered the disease to be ____________________, they held out little hope for the patient's recovery.
2. When we reflected on his long and happy life and his unmatched record of public service, we found the ____________________ comforting and even inspiring.
3. She claimed to be an unbiased witness, but I found her testimony to be opinionated and ____________________.
4. The constitution provides that the ____________________ received by the President is to be neither increased nor decreased during his term of office.
5. You should not approach a class in sex education with such a lustful and ____________________ attitude.
6. The true test of her character will be how she is able to deal with the ____________________ of life.
7. She cannot relate to other people in a constructive way because she is ____________________ in her own prejudices and hostilities.
8. At first she showed only a mild interest in checkers, but as she played more and developed skill, she became a real ____________________ of the game.
9. What good does it do to regale the prisoners with ____________________ about going straight if they have no chance to make an honest living when they are released?
10. In her speech to the entering freshman class, the dean emphasized that the benefits they derived from any course would be ____________________ with the effort that they devoted to it.

11. We found overwhelming beauty in the most common manifestations of nature, such as the colors of sunset, the delicate shape of a flower, or the ____________ wings of an insect.

12. My Classics professor said that the epic poem represents the most noble and inspiring of all literary ____________.

13. Their reverence for all creation was so great that even the most common manifestation of nature was ____________.

14. One of my fondest hopes is to visit Jerusalem, the city that has had a unique role in history as the ____________ of three world religions.

15. It was a cat-and-mouse play about a patient detective and an aristocratic jewel thief who stole with elegance and ____________.

16. The overbearing maître d' ____________ the diners into meekly accepting the least desirable table in the restaurant.

17. The omniscient narrator is probably the most common ____________ assumed by novel writers.

18. Our troops returned from their successful ____________ against the enemy's base in a jubilant mood.

19. Time after time, he rose on the floor of the Senate and delivered bitter ____________ against the lack of effective measures against environmental pollution.

20. Having been conditioned to take wealth and luxury for granted, they tended to take a(n) ____________ attitude toward money, even when they had only a modest income.

Writing: Words in Action

1. Look back at "The Comics and Cartoons of Winsor McCay" (pages 60–61). Consider the characteristics and the political and artistic impact of both print comic strips and of animated cartoons. Write a compare-and-contrast essay, using at least three details from the passage and three unit words, that helps a reader understand how the two art forms are similar and different.

2. Interactive, visual, and motion media—web sites, video games, television shows, movies—are ubiquitous today. Has technology helped artists find their voices and points of view, or has technology distracted the viewer and detracted from artists' voices and viewpoints? In a brief essay, explain your opinion with specific examples from your studies, reading (refer to pages 60–61), or personal observations and experience. Write at least three paragraphs, and use three or more words from this unit.

Vocabulary in Context

Literary Text

*The following excerpts are from novels by George Meredith. Some of the words you have studied in this unit appear in **boldface** type. Complete each statement below the excerpt by circling the letter of the correct answer.*

1. "Vernon's income would at once have been regulated **commensurately** with a new position requiring an increase. This money, money, money! ... Vernon is a man who would do fifty times more with a companion appreciating his abilities and making light of his little deficiencies." (*The Egoist*)

Commensurately means

a. minutely **c.** measurably
b. carefully **d.** correspondingly

George Meredith, an English novelist known for using the device of interior monologue

2. Densely ignorant of the sex, his nincompoopish idealizations, at other times preposterous, would now be annoying. He would probably presume on Clara's inconceivable lapse of dignity to read his master a lecture: he was quite equal to a **philippic** upon woman's rights. This man had not been afraid to say that he talked common sense to women. (*The Egoist*)

A **philippic** is NOT

a. educated **c.** fulmination
b. vocal **d.** raillery

3. Hard by their inn, close enough for a priestly **homily** to have been audible, stood a church campanile, wherein hung a Bell ... (*Diana of the Crossways*)

A **homily** is a(n)

a. verdict **c.** figure of speech
b. lecture **d.** kind of uniform

4. Dame Gossip boils. Her one idea of animation is to have her dramatis **persona** in violent motion, always the biggest foremost ... (*The Amazing Marriage*)

A dramatis **persona** is a(n)

a. character **c.** overabundance
b. outfit **d.** immodesty

5. For this she yielded the pleasures of town; for this she **immured** herself at Raynham; for this she bore with a thousand follies ... and heaven knows what forms of torture and self-denial, which are smilingly endured by that greatest of voluntary martyrs—a mother with a daughter to marry. (*The Ordeal of Richard Feverel*)

To **immure** oneself is to

a. transform **c.** confine
b. starve **d.** clothe

Snap the code, or go to **vocabularyworkshop.com**

*Read the following selection, taking note of the **boldface** words and their contexts. These words are among those you will be studying in Unit 6. As you complete the exercises in this unit, it may help to refer to the way the words are used below.*

Origins of Anarchism

<Magazine Article>

by Sonja L. Brinkan

Anarchism is an **iconoclastic** philosophy aimed at abolishing the state. Its rhetoric often takes a **contumelious** tone, and some anarchists advocate violent revolution. But the ideal society envisioned by anarchists is neither a **saturnalian** chaos nor a muddle of masses in perpetual conflict. Essentially, anarchism is motivated by a rosy, even **maudlin** vision of humanity's potential for peace, harmony, and freedom without government control. Though anarchism's goals seem unrealistic, its ideals merit attention, providing a **touchstone** by which scholars might measure social reform.

A lithograph from "Le Petit Journal" depicts an explosion in Paris, 1905.

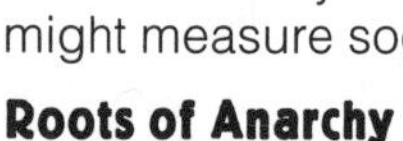

Roots of Anarchy

Many anthropologists maintain that early human society was anarchic, without government, political institutions, or strict hierarchies of power. Others counter that meaningful hierarchies existed in primitive societies, and even among chimpanzees. Anthropologists may argue, **quid pro quo**, about the prehistoric origins of anarchy. Though it picks up **in medias res**, the record of history is somewhat clearer.

With the emergence of states, strains of anarchism arose among ancient philosophers. Lao Tzu's principle of nonrule, nonaction, or nonintervention is interpreted by many as an example of anarchist thinking in ancient China because it urged nonintervention of governments. Bao Jingyan's **portentous** treatise on the evils of social hierarchy and the futility of government rule clearly displays anarchical tendencies. In Greece, Zeno of Citium argued that the ideal society is a community of free, rational individuals living without regulation by a state. Historians cite countless examples of anarchist tendencies in communal societies of the West, from Europe's Middle Ages through the American colonial period.

Modern Anarchists

William Godwin's *Enquiry Concerning Human Justice,* published in 1793, was among the first modern anarchist treatises. A man of the Enlightenment, Godwin held an optimistic view of human nature and blamed government for corrupting it. Godwin argued that government **vitiates** human character, that our vices result from social conditions imposed by government. He sought progress toward a more **salubrious** and stateless form of society, in which people's rational self-interest would lead them to act in harmony.

Pierre-Joseph Proudhon

Mikhail Bakunin

Emma Goldman

Anarchism's heyday dawned in the mid-nineteenth century; Europe was racked with **traumatic** revolutions as the continent's governments **modulated** from aristocratic monarchies to more egalitarian social orders. In 1840, Pierre-Joseph Proudhon summarized his anarchist philosophy in the **dictum** "Liberty is the mother, not the daughter, of order." He believed the best society would arise spontaneously from the action of free, rational individuals. Mikhail Bakunin argued, against Proudhon's disciples, that all productive property should be owned collectively. However, Bakunin opposed other Marxist notions that social revolutions must be led by enlightened elites in positions of authority. Instead, he believed in the power of the masses. Decades later, following the Russian Revolution, the **prescience** of Bakunin's anti-elitism was affirmed by anarchists like Emma Goldman, a Lithuanian Jewish immigrant to New York City, who criticized the Bolsheviks' authoritarian, repressive approach to social control, and loathed its rigid centralization and anti-Semitism.

Dissent and Dreams in the Sidelines of History

Anarchists played an important role in the reform of Western society for nearly a century, particularly in the labor movements of the nineteenth and early twentieth centuries. But anarchism was declining by the start of World War II. The movement's effectiveness was hampered by **internecine** disputes and by its essential paradox: How can people who passionately object to imposed social organization come together to act as a coherent political force?

The paradox reflects deeper problems with the very idea of anarchy. Hope is a waking dream, and anarchism's dream of a free society without government is unlikely to be realized. But its nobler yearnings toward social and economic equality continue to inspire reformers.

Sonja L. Brinkan is a professor of economic history at Sutton College in Arborville. Her last article for The Final Word *was "A Maverick Abroad," Vol. xxv, April 2011.*

Snap the code, or go to **vocabularyworkshop.com**

Definitions

Note the spelling, pronunciation, part(s) of speech, and definition(s) of each of the following words. Then write the word in the blank spaces in the illustrative sentence(s) following. Finally, study the lists of synonyms and antonyms.

1. abortive
(ə bôr′ tiv)

(*adj.*) failing to accomplish an intended aim or purpose; only partially or imperfectly developed

An ____________________ attempt to seize the throne ended badly for the participants.

SYNONYMS: miscarried, fruitless
ANTONYMS: realized, consummated

2. bruit
(brüt)

(*v.*) to spread news, reports, or unsubstantiated rumors

News of the company's closing and the impending job losses was immediately ____________________ about the office.

SYNONYMS: noise abroad, blazon
ANTONYMS: cover up, hush up

3. contumelious
(kon tü mē′ lē əs)

(*adj.*) insolent or rude in speech or behavior; insultingly abusive; humiliating

The ambassador's ____________________ reply was completely unexpected.

SYNONYMS: vituperative, excoriating
ANTONYMS: laudatory, commendatory, deferential

4. dictum
(dik′ təm)

(*n.*) a short saying; an authoritative statement

According to the ____________________ of the critics, the play is not worth the price of admission.

SYNONYMS: maxim, precept, aphorism, axiom

5. ensconce
(en skons′)

(*v.*) to settle comfortably and firmly in position; to put or hide in a safe place

After a very long, difficult day at work, I gratefully ____________________ myself in my snug, warm bed.

SYNONYMS: lodge, entrench
ANTONYMS: unseat, oust

6. iconoclastic
(ī kon ə klas′ tik)

(*adj.*) attacking or seeking to overthrow popular or traditional beliefs, ideas, or institutions

The writer's ____________________ opinions always seem to stir controversy.

SYNONYMS: image-breaking, irreverent, heretical
ANTONYMS: conservative, reverent, orthodox

7. in medias res
(in med′ ē əs rās′)

(*adv.*) in or into the middle of a plot; into the middle of things

Since this episode begins ______________________, we need to record it and watch the earlier installments first.

8. internecine
(int ər nes′ ēn)

(*adj.*) mutually destructive; characterized by great slaughter and bloodshed

An ______________________ feud has existed between the clans for generations.

SYNONYMS: murderous, savage, ruinous
ANTONYMS: peaceful, harmonious, constructive

9. maladroit
(mal ə droit′)

(*adj.*) lacking skill or dexterity; lacking tact, perception, or judgment

The supervisor's ______________________ interference revealed a lack of experience.

SYNONYMS: inept, awkward, gauche
ANTONYMS: dexterous, deft, tactful

10. maudlin
(môd′ lin)

(*adj.*) excessively or effusively sentimental

The tenor sang a ______________________ ballad and then a humorous ditty.

SYNONYMS: mushy, mawkish

11. modulate
(mod′ yə lāt)

(*v.*) to change or vary the intensity or pitch; to temper or soften; to regulate, adjust

Asked to ______________________ their voices, the choir responded adroitly.

SYNONYMS: adapt, moderate

12. portentous
(pôr ten′ təs)

(*adj.*) foreshadowing an event to come; causing wonder or awe; self-consciously weighty, pompous

No one realized just how ______________________ the strange events of last week would turn out to be.

SYNONYMS: foreboding, ominous, pretentious
ANTONYMS: auspicious, encouraging, propitious

13. prescience
(presh′ əns)

(*n.*) knowledge of events or actions before they happen; foresight

The detectives were skeptical about the psychic's ______________________ of the suspect's next crime.

SYNONYM: foreknowledge
ANTONYM: hindsight

14. quid pro quo (kwid′ prō kwō′)

(*n.*) something given in exchange or return for something else

Before agreeing to give their support, the representatives insisted on some ____________________.

SYNONYMS: swap, trade

15. salubrious (sə lü′ brē əs)

(*adj.*) conducive to health or well-being; wholesome

Seeking the ____________________ effects of sea air, the family headed for a shore vacation.

SYNONYMS: healthy, invigorating
ANTONYMS: harmful, unhealthy, deleterious, noxious

16. saturnalian (sat ər nā′ lyan)

(*adj.*) characterized by riotous or unrestrained revelry or licentiousness

The boisterously ____________________ spectacle was truly something to behold, even from a distance.

SYNONYMS: dissipated, debauched, orgiastic
ANTONYMS: prim, decorous, sedate, seemly

17. touchstone (təch′ stōn)

(*n.*) a means of testing worth or genuineness

A work's popularity among succeeding generations is thought to be a ____________________ of its merit.

SYNONYMS: criterion, benchmark, yardstick

18. traumatic (trau̇ mat′ ik)

(*adj.*) so shocking to the emotions as to cause lasting and substantial psychological damage

People may feel the effects of a ____________________ experience for years afterward.

SYNONYM: jolting
ANTONYMS: soothing, comforting, pleasant, agreeable

19. vitiate (vish′ ē āt)

(*v.*) to weaken, debase, or corrupt; to impair the quality or value of

____________________ by its lack of managerial skill, the company's fortunes went straight downhill.

SYNONYM: degrade
ANTONYMS: purify, fortify, strengthen, enhance

20. waggish (wag′ ish)

(*adj.*) fond of making jokes; characteristic of a joker; playfully humorous or droll

The innkeeper's ____________________ stories lifted the flagging spirits of the weary travelers.

SYNONYM: whimsical
ANTONYMS: serious, grave, grim, humorless

Choosing the Right Word

*Select the **boldface** word that better completes each sentence. You might refer to the selection on pages 70–71 to see how most of these words are used in context.*

By the end of 1905, the Wright brothers had designed a plane that could fly for at least 39 minutes.

1. Prior to the Wright brothers' first successful airplane flight in 1903, all of mankind's efforts to fly had been (**internecine, abortive**).
2. Although those supposedly (**abortive, waggish**) remarks were dressed in the guise of humor, they betrayed a strong undertone of resentment.
3. The concessions that we are making are manifest, but I do not perceive a reasonable (**prescience, quid pro quo**) from the other side.
4. All the snide rumors that have been spread about them do not (**vitiate, ensconce**) their solid reputation for authentic kindness and decency.
5. They survived the critical years due to their uncanny (**prescience, touchstone**) that enabled them to anticipate the moves of their enemies.
6. In that situation, I don't know which was more distressing—the callous indifference of some of my "friends" or the (**maudlin, contumelious**) sympathy of others.
7. The decline in the value of the company's stock was attributed to the fact that rumors of a contract cancellation had been widely (**bruited, vitiated**).
8. In her volume of fairy tales, the great creatures of (**portentous, salubrious**) size were both gentle giants and fire-breathing dragons.
9. I felt that I had stated my case with sincerity and conviction, but my heart sank when they reacted with a (**maladroit, portentous**) silence.
10. My plan to run in the primaries will not be diverted by the (**touchstone, dicta**) of so-called experts who assert that I have no chance of winning.
11. Historians believe that the Civil War had a collective (**traumatic, salubrious**) impact, which was not healed until a new generation had grown to maturity.
12. Willy-nilly, parents often enter (**in medias res, waggishly**) into a quarrel between siblings, especially when lasting damage seems about to occur.
13. Some people seem to be natural nonconformists; for them (**prescience, iconoclasm**) is not just a mood or an affectation but a way of life.
14. When the miners arrived with all of their back pay and intent upon "having fun," our town soon took on the aspect of a frontier (**saturnalia, quid pro quo**).
15. With her elegance and remarkable feel for style, is it any wonder that she soon became (**modulated, ensconced**) as the arbiter of fashion?

16. Their cool and detached skepticism now struck me as a(n) (**iconoclastic, salubrious**) factor in that highly emotionalized situation.

17. The cat (**ensconced, bruited**) herself in safety behind the coats.

18. In spite of my extreme nervousness, I made every effort to (**modulate, bruit**) my voice and speak the first lines in a calm, controlled manner.

19. Their efforts to settle the differences between the two factions were so (**portentous, maladroit**) that what had begun as a rift became a chasm.

20. Homer's *Iliad* begins (**quid pro quo, in medias res**) with a dramatic argument between Agamemnon and Achilles during the Trojan War.

21. My mother passed on her greatest wisdom with the following (**prescience, dictum**): Treat others as you wish to be treated.

22. Warfare has become too (**internecine, saturnalian**) to risk.

23. While the organizations's goal is ultimately free trade, each state must have the freedom to (**modulate, vitiate**) trade based on its interests.

24. A strict sense of honesty, marked by a refusal to take refuge in clever ambiguities, has been the (**touchstone, dictum**) of my career in politics.

25. Her (**abortive, contumelious**) attempt to ruin our plans was malicious but unsuccessful.

Choose the word from this unit that is the same or most nearly the same in meaning as the **boldface** *word or expression in the phrase. Write that word on the line. Use a dictionary if necessary.*

1. a **beneficial** aspect of the trip ____________________
2. would **undermine** all our achievements ____________________
3. **clumsy** efforts at reconciliation ____________________
4. his **jocular** mood was contagious ____________________
5. undone by a lack of **foresight** ____________________
6. one debater's **scurrilous** remarks ____________________
7. **nestled** in a favorite chair ____________________
8. made a **premature** attempt ____________________
9. quickly **broadcast** the results ____________________
10. moved by the **sentimental** story ____________________

Antonyms

*Choose the word from this unit that is most nearly opposite in meaning to the **boldface** word or expression in the phrase. Write that word on the line. Use a dictionary if necessary.*

1. please **conceal** the rumors that school is cancelled ____________
2. a **successful** attempt to scale the wall ____________
3. **displace** herself and move away from home ____________
4. **skillful** footwork on the dance floor ____________
5. a **dour** group waiting at the ticket window ____________

Completing the Sentence

From the words in this unit, choose the one that best completes each of the following sentences. Write the word in the space provided.

1. I was an extremely sensitive child, and the death of my beloved mother certainly had a(n) ____________ effect upon me.
2. If you are so ____________ in handling your own personal affairs, how can you presume to advise others how to manage their lives?
3. It is one thing to offer a personal opinion; it is quite another to issue a(n) ____________ as though you are the only one with any knowledge of the subject.
4. And such are the quirks of fate that there Maria was, after all her mishaps and blunders, firmly ____________ as the president of the firm.
5. In our bored and depressed mood, her buoyant personality had a most ____________ effect.
6. The coach devised a clever strategy, but it proved ____________ when our team failed to execute it properly.
7. Though the guests at the gala benefit tried to maintain an air of cheer, the ____________ news of the international crisis hung like a pall over the gathering.
8. A group of elderly people sitting about sipping tea and discussing the weather is scarcely my idea of ____________ revelry.
9. The speaker paid no attention to the ____________ remarks of a few hecklers in the crowd but went right on with her speech.
10. As she thoroughly enjoys taking potshots at sacred cows, I'd describe her attitude as definitely ____________.

11. How can you expect them to cooperate with us unless they receive some reasonable __________________ for their efforts?

12. For years, Churchill's warnings about Hitler were dismissed as alarmism; only after the outbreak of World War II did people appreciate his __________________.

13. I certainly have no intention of turning my back on them simply because it has been __________________ about town they are involved in some sort of scandal.

14. If he would only devote more time in school to serious study and less to __________________ pranks, his grades would probably improve.

15. All the evidence presented at such length by their lawyers does not seriously __________________ the case against the accused.

16. The deathbed scene might have been effective if it had been played with restraint, but their woefully ham-handed acting turned it into a(n) __________________ tearjerker.

17. What we are facing in this organization is not healthy competition among the executives but a(n) __________________ struggle that will destroy the company.

18. To gain the immediate attention of the reader, the short-story writer sometimes begins a narrative __________________, rather than at the very beginning of events.

19. More than anything else, the ability to create distinctive characters and make them come alive on the page is the __________________ of a great novelist.

20. Though the critic still has nothing good to say about modern art, age and experience have somewhat __________________ the intensity of his disapproval.

Writing: Words in Action

1. In "Origins of Anarchism" (pages 70–71), the writer asks, "How can people who passionately object to social organization come together to act as a coherent political force?" Write your answer to this question, explaining *whether* such people can come together and, then, *how* they can or *why* they cannot come together. Use at least three details from the passage and three unit words.

2. *"Someone has said that it requires less mental effort to condemn than to think. The widespread mental indolence, so prevalent in society, proves this to be only too true. Rather than to go to the bottom of any given idea, to examine into its origin and meaning, most people will either condemn it altogether, or rely on some superficial or prejudicial definition of non-essentials."—Emma Goldman*

   Do you agree with Goldman? In a brief essay, explain your opinion with specific examples from your studies, reading (refer to pages 70–71), or personal observations and experience. Write at least three paragraphs, and use three or more words from this unit.

Vocabulary in Context
Literary Text

The following excerpts are from Henry David Thoreau's works Walden *and* A Week on the Concord and Merrimack Rivers. *Some of the words you have studied in this unit appear in* **boldface** *type. Complete each statement below the excerpt by circling the letter of the correct answer.*

1. It was the only battle which I have ever witnessed, the only battlefield I ever trod while the battle was raging; **internecine** war; the red republicans on the one hand, and the black imperialists on the other. (*Walden*)

An **internecine** war is

a. abbreviated **c.** deleterious for all
b. interminable **d.** injurious to a few

2. There came to me in this case a melody which the air had strained, and which had conversed with every leaf and needle of the wood, that portion of the sound which the elements had taken up and **modulated** and echoed from vale to vale. (*Walden*)

A **modulated** sound is

a. systematic **c.** fortified
b. divided **d.** adjusted

A replica of Henry David Thoreau's one-room cabin stands by Walden Pond.

3. Or I was attracted by the passage of wild pigeons from this wood to that, with a slight quivering winnowing sound and carrier haste; or from under a rotten stump my hoe turned up a sluggish **portentous** and outlandish spotted salamander, a trace of Egypt and the Nile, yet our contemporary. (*Walden*)

Something that is **portentous** is

a. awe-inspiring **c.** immense
b. alluring **d.** miniscule

4. If we knew all the laws of Nature, we should need only one fact, or the description of one actual phenomenon, to infer all the particular results at that point. Now we know only a few laws, and our result is **vitiated** ... by our ignorance of essential elements in the calculation. (*Walden*)

A result that is **vitiated** is NOT

a. spoiled **c.** impeded
b. debased **d.** improved

5. Dreams are the **touchstones** of our characters. We are scarcely less afflicted when we remember some unworthiness in our conduct in a dream, than if it had been actual, and the intensity of our grief, which is our atonement, measures the degree by which this is separated from an actual unworthiness. (*A Week on the Concord and Merrimack Rivers*)

A **touchstone** is a(n)

a. interior **c.** foresight
b. criterion **d.** opening

Snap the code, or go to **vocabularyworkshop.com**

Vocabulary for Comprehension

*Read the following selection in which some of the words you have studied in Units 4–6 appear in **boldface** type. Then answer the questions on page 81.*

Pinning down historical facts can be tricky, as this passage about the invention of eyeglasses demonstrates.

(Line)

By the end of the thirteenth century, people began to see the world in a new light, for it was about that time that eyeglasses were (5) invented. But **forays** into the question of precisely when they were invented and by whom have been inconclusive, **tendentious**, and filled with intrigue.

(10) Researchers have put forth candidates from several European countries and China. Although the exact identity of the inventor has not as yet been established conclusively, (15) he or she was most likely an Italian glassblower working in the 1280s. The evidence favors either Alessandro Spina or Salvino Armato, with a slight edge to Armato. Armato (20) was an optical physicist who is believed to have contrived correcting lenses to improve his own vision.

In 1289, the Italian writer Sandro di Popozo refers to eyeglasses as (25) having "recently been invented." Popozo writes about the advantages afforded by the lenses but never mentions the inventor's name. A second reference appears seventeen (30) years later in a sermon by the friar Giordano di Rivalto. In the sermon, the friar refers to the nearly 20-year-old art of making eyeglasses. He, too, neglects to provide us with the (35) name of the inventor.

No matter who invented them, spectacles caught on quickly. But they were not for everybody. The high cost kept them from **hoi polloi**, (40) and the fact that all lenses were convex made these "eye disks" "**elixirs**" for the farsighted only. (Concave lenses, which help the nearsighted, first appeared more (45) than a century later.) In addition, the lenses were hard to wear. The now-familiar stiff frames that loop over the wearer's ears were not developed for another 400 years.

(50) Despite the limitations of these early eyeglasses, sales were brisk, and Italian craftspeople churned them out. The rest is history.

1. The meaning of **forays** (line 5) is
a. looks
b. retreats
c. relays
d. ventures
e. attacks

2. **Tendentious** (line 8) most nearly means
a. tentative
b. impartial
c. libelous
d. cantankerous
e. partisan

3. The primary purpose of the passage is
a. to refute
b. to persuade
c. to explain
d. to entertain
e. to reflect

4. According to paragraph 2 (lines 10–22), eyeglasses were probably invented
a. by Alessandro Spina
b. by an Italian glassblower in the 1280s
c. by a friar named Giordano di Rivalto
d. by the Italian writer Sandro di Popozo
e. in China

5. The evidence cited in paragraph 3 (lines 23–35) serves primarily to
a. strengthen the theory that eyeglasses were invented during the 1280s
b. reveal the writer's skepticism as a historian
c. refute the reliability of Sandro di Popozo and Giordano di Rivalto
d. establish the writer's credentials as an expert on the subject
e. confirm that Salvino Armato invented eyeglasses

6. Which of the following best describes the organizational structure of paragraph 4 (lines 36–49)?
a. order of importance
b. order of impression
c. comparison and contrast
d. cause and effect
e. chronological order

7. **Hoi polloi** (line 39) is best defined as
a. masses
b. merchants
c. elite
d. clergy
e. royalty

8. The meaning of **elixirs** (line 42) is
a. prophesies
b. lenses
c. cure-alls
d. tools
e. accessories

9. According to the author, concave lenses first appeared
a. about twenty years after the invention of convex lenses
b. in the 1500s
c. in the 1600s
d. when prices for convex lenses started to decrease
e. more than a century after the invention of convex lenses

10. Which would be the most appropriate vehicle for publishing this passage?
a. a brief magazine article
b. a letter to a newspaper editor
c. an article in a technical journal
d. an ad for an optician's shop
e. an entry in a travel guide to Italy

11. From the passage, you can infer that
a. there were few nearsighted people in the thirteenth century
b. few, if any, poor people owned the new "eye disks"
c. Alessandro Spina became famous
d. microscopes were invented at the same time as eyeglasses
e. few, if any, Chinese people had eyeglasses in the 1200s or 1300s

12. The main purpose of paragraph 4 (lines 36–49) is to
a. reiterate the main idea
b. tell how convex lenses were made
c. tell why many didn't buy eyeglasses
d. explain how it was difficult to design comfortable eyewear
e. prove eyeglasses were not popular

Two-Word Completions

Select the pair of words that best complete the meaning of each of the following passages.

1. When he realized that flattery was getting him nowhere, he attempted to ________________ me into acquiescence; but, here again, his efforts proved ________________.

a. bruit . . . risible
b. browbeat . . . abortive
c. vitiate . . . tendentious
d. modulate . . . maladroit

2. Famous for his daring ________________ deep behind Northern lines, J. E. B. Stuart, the South's most colorful cavalry commander, led his men on one dangerous mission after another with all the ________________ and style of one of Charlemagne's legendary paladins.

a. obsequies . . . persona
b. emoluments . . . prescience
c. philippics . . . derring-do
d. forays . . . panache

3. In one of her more devastating ________________, Dorothy Parker is reputed to have once observed that an incompetent actor's interpretation of a role ran the ________________ of emotions from A to B.

a. dicta . . . gamut
b. lucubrations . . . mnemonic
c. corollaries . . . cul-de-sac
d. homilies . . . parameters

4. Though I can't say that I relish the thriller as a literary form, I'm a real ________________ of the detective ________________.

a. pundit . . . touchstone
b. iconoclast . . . matrix
c. aficionado . . . genre
d. persona . . . folderol

5. My late night ________________ on the meaning of my life and my role as office worker, I fear, are ________________ of a general displeasure with my current position.

a. obsequies . . . portentous
b. emoluments . . . insouciant
c. lucubrations . . . symptomatic
d. mnemonics . . . ineffable

6. My aunt delighted in creating ________________ comic strips that made visual the moral principles she valued; however, she made sure that her readers did not feel as if she were delivering a weekly ________________.

a. waggish . . . homily
b. saturnalian . . . prescience
c. contumelious . . . quid pro quo
d. bilious . . . corollary

7. Because French, Spanish, and Italian are ________________ languages, in college I quickly and happily ________________ myself in the study of Romantic languages, as I had studied Spanish in middle school and high school.

a. interstices . . . liturgy
b. cognate . . . ensconced
c. persiflage . . . plethora
d. maudlin . . . vitiated

Adages

In the passage "Origins of Anarchism" (see pages 70–71), the writer proclaims, "Hope is a waking dream," and goes on to say that, while the realization of anarchism is unlikely, the ideal of anarchism will continue to inspire.

"Hope is a waking dream" is an **adage**, or a short statement that expresses a general or accepted truth. For example, the statement in the unit opener passage means that to have hope is to experience the thoughts and wonder commonplace in those dreams from which we do not wish to wake.

Choosing the Right Adage

*Read each sentence. Use context clues to figure out the meaning of each adage in **boldface** print. Then write the letter of the definition for the adage in the sentence.*

1. When her daughter would not wash her hair, the mother replied, "**Cleanliness is next to godliness.**" _______
2. Antoine asked why Jane finally bought a cell phone. Jane replied, "**If you can't beat them, join them.**" _______
3. Did you know that 95 percent of the world's animals are invertebrates? **Fact is stranger than fiction**. _______
4. That bicycle I bought online broke immediately. "**Let the buyer beware**," I say. _______
5. We will soon be faced with another economic depression because **history repeats itself**. _______
6. She still forgets to recycle her office paper. I suppose **old habits die hard**, and we have a long way to go. _______
7. I told my grandpa, "**It's never too late to learn**. I will help you scan your old photos to the computer!" _______
8. "**Stop and smell the roses**," I advised him. "You've been working 60-hour weeks for too long!" _______
9. You need to enjoy yourself and spend some of that money in your savings account. **You can't take it with you**. _______
10. I do want to go to your party, but my sister is moving and needs my help. **Blood is thicker than water**. _______

a. Enjoy your wealth now; you have no things after you die.
b. True events are often harder to believe than made-up stories.
c. You can always learn something new.
d. Join with those who have far more power than you have.
e. It is difficult to change one's behavior or routines.
f. It is important to keep clean.
g. Take time to enjoy life and its pleasures.
h. Family is more important than any other relationship.
i. The same events appear to happen again and again.
j. When you buy something, be careful.

Writing with Adages

Find the meaning of each adage. (Use an online or print dictionary if necessary.) Then write a sentence for each adage.

1. A chain is only as strong as its weakest link.

____

2. Children are a poor man's riches.

____

3. It's always darkest just before the dawn.

____

4. There is honor among thieves.

____

5. There's always room at the top.

____

____

6. The eyes are the window to the soul.

____

____

7. The exception proves the rule.

____

____

8. The bigger they come, the harder they fall.

____

9. Tomorrow is another day.

____

10. Silence is golden.

____

11. The best things in life are free.

____

12. Fine feathers make fine birds.

____

Denotation and Connotation

Words always have **denotations**, or dictionary definitions. Words can also have numerous **connotations**, or subjective meanings. A word often has a *positive* or *negative* connotation.

Skilled writers use nuance in denotation and connotation to communicate carefully. For example, to describe a confident character, a writer might describe her as *bold, daring, presumptuous, reckless, audacious,* or *plucky*. Each word conveys a different message.

Consider these synonyms for the relatively negative word *maudlin*:

sentimental *effusive* *mushy* *mawkish*

Sentimental has a somewhat neutral connotation, suggesting someone who can easily become emotional. *Effusive* often has a positive connotation and can show approval for abundance of emotion. *Mushy* has a negative connotation, and *mawkish* is so negative that it conveys a feeling of disgust.

Think: A sentimental love story might be a pleasure to read, while a mushy love story might be unpleasant due to an annoying overabundance of tear-jerking moments that feel false.

Look at these examples of words that are similar in denotation but have different connotations.

NEUTRAL	POSITIVE	NEGATIVE
authority	**aficionado**	**fanatic**
compel	**suggest**	**browbeat**
inexpert	**coltish**	**maladroit**

Comprehending a word's denotation and its connotations is an important skill to develop. Effective writers and speakers develop this skill.

Shades of Meaning

Write a plus sign (+) in the box if the word has a positive connotation. Write a minus sign (–) if the word has a negative connotation. Put a zero (0) if the word is neutral.

1. salubrious ☐ **2.** folderol ☐ **3.** gamut ☐ **4.** hoi polloi ☐

5. parameter ☐ **6.** bilious ☐ **7.** derring-do ☐ **8.** traumatic ☐

9. bruit ☐ **10.** corollary ☐ **11.** ensconce ☐ **12.** contumelious ☐

13. in medias res ☐ **14.** internecine ☐ **15.** saturnalian ☐ **16.** waggish ☐

Expressing the Connotation

Read each sentence. Select the word in parentheses that expresses the connotation (positive, negative, or neutral) given at the beginning of the sentence.

neutral 1. The teachers' effectiveness was (**vitiated, weakened**) when the class sizes were increased.

negative 2. The mayor delivered a (**lecture, philippic**) to end the strike.

neutral 3. My speech concerning the proposed seat belt law was (**partisan, tendentious**) but honest.

positive 4. Her (**sheer, diaphanous**) and lustrous dress was sleeveless and wowed the photographers.

positive 5. The (**ineffable, indescribable**) beauty of Lake Superior may only be expressed in poetic verse.

negative 6. The black and (**portentous, ominous**) gathering storm clouds reflected the darkness our family faced.

negative 7. The (**obloquy, reproach**) endured by the journalist was what first motivated him, thankfully, to resign.

positive 8. Your words of kindness were the necessary (**elixir, remedy**) that gave me, at once, both hope and peace.

Challenge: Using Connotation

Choose vocabulary words from Units 4–6 to replace the highlighted words in the sentences below. Then explain how the connotation of the replacement word changes the tone of the sentence.

divination	**prurient**	**maladroit**
touchstone	**obsequies**	**affinity**

1. Last year, the reporter predicted a downturn, a now celebrated **guess** ____________________, when all other experts predicted the economy's expansion.

____

____

2. There was mutual **understanding** ____________________ between the two schoolmates that lasted throughout their lives.

____

____

3. The waiter's **tactless** ____________________ service was only the beginning of an unpleasant evening out; the night culminated in us missing the movie.

____

____

Classical Roots

gen— race, kind, class; origin, birth

This root appears in **genre**, "a type, class, or variety, especially with relation to literary composition or painting" (page 63). Some other words based on the same root are listed below.

carcinogen	**degenerate**	**generic**	**genocide**
congenital	**genealogy**	**genesis**	**homogeneous**

From the list of words above, choose the one that corresponds to each of the brief definitions below. Write the word in the blank space in the illustrative sentence below the definition.

1. uniform in composition; like in nature or kind

The Latin Club is comprised of a remarkably ____________________ group of students.

2. relating to an entire group or class; not protected by trademark, nonproprietary

We know many products by their brands but not by their ____________________ names.

3. creation, origin; the coming into being of something

No one is entirely sure of the ____________________ of the idea that became the Internet we know today.

4. to deteriorate or decline physically or morally; exhibiting such decline; a morally degraded person

The judge condemned their ____________________ behavior by imposing a stiff sentence.

5. a record or account of a family's or a person's descent; lineage; the study of ancestry and family histories

Using online resources, he was able to trace his ____________________ back ten generations.

6. the systematic extermination of a racial, political, or cultural group

During the regime of Pol Pot (1975–1979), Khmer Rouge forces in Cambodia conducted a ____________________ of unprecedented proportions.

7. cancer-causing substance

Food additives cannot be used unless they pass tests proving that they are not ____________________.

8. existing at birth; constituting an essential characteristic as if by birth, inherent

No amount of guidance and counseling could overcome the fact that she was simply a ____________________ liar.

UNIT 7

*Read the following selection, taking note of the **boldface** words and their contexts. These words are among those you will be studying in Unit 7. As you complete the exercises in this unit, it may help to refer to the way the words are used below.*

On the Edge

<First-Person Narrative>

"There's nothing in the world like a Class V river after spring melt," my friends assured me, recounting tales of **picaresque** adventures on the river last spring.

"It's living on the edge," they said, and I really couldn't tell if they were trying to get me scared or pumped up.

As we unpacked our kayaks, they were hollering and laughing, frenetic, **gamboling** around the site; I was excited too, but less boisterous, trying to concentrate my energy. It would be my first time on a river this rough, but if I was nervous, I wasn't **ambivalent**: I'd been envisioning this moment for years, and could not wait to hit the water. Besides, I knew my friends wouldn't give me **carte blanche**; they'd lead the way, and I'd follow, guided by the greater experience of my companions.

From the moment we put into the river, I was **imbued** with a profound awe at its power—I mean, I'm fit and strong, but it took every ounce of strength to control that boat, **refractory** under the river's influence, till after ten minutes of wrestling against the vessel and the water I was exhausted. Looking ahead, I took some comfort from the sight of my friends' boats skipping over the rolling foam.

That moment of consolation might have broken my focus, because, before I could react, an **inchoate** wall of froth raged up from the river, an angry ghost, and the whole world disappeared. I couldn't see my friends, or the banks, or the cliffs beyond—worse, I didn't see that execrable hole coming, that roiling **cataclysm** of backwash, till it had already snatched and swallowed me whole. Fierce currents slapped me from every side; I flapped, helpless, like a salmon in grizzly jaws; upright, underwater, upright,

underwater, upside-down, I don't know how many times that kayak and I capsized and came right again.

Beleaguered by surging waters, my normal, everyday brain chemistry fallen into **abeyance**, I was running on pure adrenalin. Staring into the icy eyes of the abyss, my body wrestled with the river, which seemed a living thing, pushing against me, forcing me deeper underwater, torturing that **malleable** kayak till I thought it would snap like a toy. But with a furious final slap my bow dove deep, we caught a downstream current, and I lurched out of the hole.

My strength was sapped, my stomach **queasy**, and a fast glance downriver did nothing to revive my spirits. White water churned through a bouldery maze; my friends were gone from sight. I'd already taken a pounding, and the stretch ahead seemed just as rough. I could have **opted** to swim to the bank but decided against it: If I got out of that kayak, one of the approaching boulders might prove too quick a **nemesis**.

Those scraggy boulders nearly got me anyway, but I worked my way through them in a frantic blur of paddling. Relieved, I exhaled hard, groaning and laughing in one breath—unaware was out of the frying pan and into t My ears, still ringing from the ordeal i hole, didn't hear the commotion of the approaching roar, and my gaze was riveted on my friends, just now come into view, standing and gesticulating wildly on the left bank. They'd seen the waterfall ahead, and—normally none too **fastidious** about avoiding risks—they'd judged the drop too dangerous and paddled ashore rather than chance the fall. Too late to join them—the swirling current swept me over the brink.

One good thing about plunging over a waterfall is that it doesn't take long. There were three drops, and I went airborne three times, and somehow I thwacked miraculously down and upright into splashing water at each drop's end. I can hardly take credit for it, but to any observer the feat must have seemed accomplished with some **éclat**.

"You all right?" my friends shouted, scrambling down the rocks to where I finally returned to the bank.

The reply rolled from my lips with euphoric **savoir-faire**.

"Living on the edge is fine," I panted, "but don't ever go over it."

Snap the code, or go to **vocabularyworkshop.com**

Note the spelling, pronunciation, part(s) of speech, and definition(s) of each of the following words. Then write the word in the blank spaces in the illustrative sentence(s) following. Finally, study the lists of synonyms and antonyms.

(ə bā′ əns)

(*n.*) a state of being temporarily inactive, suspended, or set aside

The administrators and staff reluctantly agreed to hold the matter in ____________________.

SYNONYMS: postponement, suspension

2. ambivalent
(am biv′ ə lənt)

(*adj.*) having opposite and conflicting feelings about someone or something

Despite their deeply ____________________ attitudes, the scientists went ahead with the program.

SYNONYMS: ambiguous, of two minds
ANTONYMS: unequivocal, unambiguous, clear-cut

3. beleaguer
(bi lē′ gər)

(*v.*) to set upon from all sides; to surround with an army; to trouble, harass

Sherman's division arrived by train, then positioned itself to ____________________ the city's fortress.

SYNONYMS: besiege, encircle, pester

4. carte blanche
(kärt′ blänsh′)

(*n.*) full freedom or authority to act at one's own discretion

The boss gave us ____________________ in the matter of how we were going to approach the client.

SYNONYM: blank check

5. cataclysm
(kat′ ə kliz əm)

(*n.*) a sudden, violent, or devastating upheaval; a surging flood, deluge

Diplomacy could not stop the ____________________ of World War I.

SYNONYMS: disaster, catastrophe

6. debauch
(di bôch′)

(*v.*) to corrupt morally, seduce; to indulge in dissipation; (*n.*) an act or occasion of dissipation or vice

Those who would ____________________ the innocent deserve our wrath.

The ____________________ began at midnight.

SYNONYMS: (*v.*) carouse, (*n.*) orgy
ANTONYMS: (*v.*) elevate, uplift, purify

7. éclat (ā klä')

(*n.*) dazzling or conspicuous success or acclaim; great brilliance (of performance or achievement)

Dazzled by the ____________________ of the performance, critics heaped praise on the troupe.

SYNONYM: celebrity
ANTONYMS: dullness, insipidity, mediocrity

8. fastidious (fa stid' ē əs)

(*adj.*) overly demanding or hard to please; excessively careful in regard to details; easily disgusted

Known for her ____________________ taste, the decorator was always in great demand.

SYNONYMS: precise, exacting, finicky
ANTONYMS: careless, sloppy, messy, untidy, slovenly

9. gambol (gam' bəl)

(*v.*) to jump or skip about playfully

The children began to ____________________ like fawns in a meadow.

SYNONYMS: frolic, romp, cavort, caper
ANTONYMS: lumber, plod

10. imbue (im byü')

(*v.*) to soak or stain thoroughly; to fill the mind

The celebrated teacher strove to ____________________ her students with the desire to succeed.

SYNONYMS: infuse, inculcate
ANTONYMS: remove, expunge, eradicate, erase

11. inchoate (in kō' it)

(*adj.*) just beginning; not fully shaped or formed

At first a molten and ____________________ mass, it soon grew, picked up speed, and destroyed all in its path.

SYNONYMS: incipient, embryonic
ANTONYMS: mature, developed, complete

12. lampoon (lam pün')

(*n.*) a malicious satire; (*v.*) to satirize, ridicule

Their ____________________ of his speech impediment did not amuse the dictator.

The intent was to ____________________ the senator.

SYNONYMS: (*n.*) burlesque; (*v.*) parody
ANTONYMS: (*n.*) compliment, flattery

13. malleable (mal' ē ə bəl)

(*adj.*) capable of being formed into different shapes; capable of being altered, adapted, or influenced

The ____________________ minds of the young students were at the mercy of the charismatic professor.

SYNONYMS: pliable, impressionable, adaptable
ANTONYMS: rigid, inflexible, unyielding, intractable

14. nemesis
(nem′ ə sis)

(*n.*) an agent or force inflicting vengeance or punishment; retribution itself; an unbeatable rival

Calculus proved to be my ____________________.

SYNONYMS: comeuppance, avenger
ANTONYMS: guardian angel, ally, patron

15. opt
(opt)

(*v.*) to make a choice or decision

We had to ____________________ for the cheaper model.

SYNONYMS: choose, select, decide

16. philistine
(fil′ i stēn)

(*adj.*) lacking in, hostile to, or smugly indifferent to cultural and artistic values or refinements; (*n.*) such a person

Their ____________________ contempt for art is something the curator simply cannot abide.

The mayor is seen as a ____________________ by the members of the city's arts community.

SYNONYMS: (*adj.*) boorish, lowbrow; (*n.*) pedant
ANTONYMS: (*adj.*) refined, cultivated; (*n.*) highbrow

17. picaresque
(pik ə resk′)

(*adj.*) involving or characteristic of clever rogues or adventurers

Reviewers cited the ____________________ element in the novel as its best feature.

SYNONYMS: roguish, rascally, rakish

18. queasy
(kwē′ zē)

(*adj.*) nauseated or uneasy; causing nausea or uneasiness; troubled

The remarks gave me a ____________________ feeling in the pit of my stomach.

SYNONYM: unsettled
ANTONYMS: calm, untroubled, confident

19. refractory
(ri frak′ tə rē)

(*adj.*) stubborn; hard or difficult to manage; not responsive to treatment or cure

Caring for the ____________________ patient left us exhausted and drained.

SYNONYMS: unruly, disobedient, willful, mulish
ANTONYMS: docile, tractable, obedient

20. savoir-faire
(sav wär fâr′)

(*n.*) the ability to say and do the right thing in any situation; social competence

The experienced and wily ambassador handled the delicate affair with her usual ____________________.

SYNONYMS: tact, finesse, suavity, sophistication
ANTONYMS: tactlessness, gaucherie, boorishness

Choosing the Right Word

*Select the **boldface** word that better completes each sentence. You might refer to the selection on pages 88–89 to see how most of these words are used in context.*

Writer and cartoonist James Thurber is most famous for his short story "The Secret Life of Walter Mitty."

1. James Thurber's stories are extremely funny, but they are also (**imbued, debauched**) with a profound sense of the pathos of the human condition.

2. Because Thurber combines humor and pathos so masterfully, we might say that the mood of his stories is (**malleable, ambivalent**).

3. Their obsession with military conquest, leading them to waste their vast resources on armaments and endless wars, proved to be their (**nemesis, gambol**).

4. Another world war would be a(n) (**éclat, cataclysm**) on so vast a scale that it is doubtful whether civilization could survive it.

5. Although his poetry is somewhat crude and (**inchoate, fastidious**), it has a primitive energy and drive that many readers find extremely appealing.

6. Instead of endless lamentations about how bad things are, let us try to look realistically at the (**lampoons, options**) open to us.

7. In spite of his courage and love of adventure, he lacks the stature of a true hero; his character might better be described as (**picaresque, abeyant**).

8. Their (**fastidious, ambivalent**) preoccupation with minor details of style is not to be confused with a genuine feeling for language.

9. Perhaps you hope to divert our attention from your own misconduct by maliciously (**lampooning, gamboling**) a sincere and able public official.

10. She was bewildered by the exhibition of abstract art, but, fearing to be labeled a (**lampoon, philistine**), she pretended to understand what she was looking at.

11. Since they had always been reasonably well-behaved, I was utterly taken aback by the twins' (**ambivalent, refractory**) behavior.

12. Although we disagreed with much of what you said, we could not help admiring the rhetorical brilliance and (**cataclysm, éclat**) of your writing style.

13. With all the misplaced confidence of inexperienced youth, I set out to make a million dollars by (**gamboling, imbuing**) in the not-so-verdant pastures of Wall Street.

14. Would it not be a gross miscarriage of justice to prosecute us under a law which, for all practical purposes, has been in (**abeyance, carte blanche**) since the early years of the last century?

15. He will never realize his full athletic potential as long as he remains (**beleaguered, opted**) by doubts about his own ability.

16. In the last analysis, all lines of authority and responsibility lead back to the President; he cannot give (**carte blanche, nemesis**) to any assistant.

17. With plenty of free time and with an excellent library at my disposal, I gave myself (**cataclysm, carte blanche**) to read anything I wanted.

18. Perhaps she felt disturbed at the prospect of having to betray her friends, but she seems to have overcome her (**queasiness, éclat**) without too much trouble.

19. Refusing to become flustered, she handled the embarrassing situation with the finesse and (**queasiness, savoir-faire**) of a born diplomat.

20. It is one thing to be open-minded and (**queasy, malleable**); it is quite another to be without fixed ideas or principles of any kind.

21. The student-run university newspaper is decidedly a(n) (**éclat, lampoon**), and their reporters relish in poking fun at the student government and the administration.

22. During World War II, in the (**gamboled, beleaguered**) city of Leningrad, employees and citizens worked tirelessly to protect art in the State Hermitage Museum.

23. Scientists have synthesized a new and durable metal compound that is both magnetic and extremely (**fastidious, malleable**) at room temperature.

24. The previously (**refractory, malleable**) case of dandruff was ameliorated thanks to the prescription shampoo and a change in the patient's diet.

25. I think the widespread use of technology in schools (**debauches, imbues**) the youth.

Synonyms

*Choose the word from this unit that is the same or most nearly the same in meaning as the **boldface** word or expression in the phrase. Write that word on the line. Use a dictionary if necessary.*

1. was in its **rudimentary** form at that time ____________________
2. welcomed the **deferment** ____________________
3. did not participate in the **spree** ____________________
4. **instill** the troops with courage ____________________
5. proceeded to **ridicule** the speaker ____________________
6. offered us **free rein** ____________________
7. **harass** the messenger of bad news ____________________
8. dresses in a **meticulous** manner ____________________
9. an **equivocal** response ____________________
10. unappreciated by the crowd of **yahoos** ____________________

*Choose the word from this unit that is most nearly opposite in meaning to the **boldface** word or expression in the phrase. Write that word on the line. Use a dictionary if necessary.*

1. a family of **aesthetes** who read voraciously ______________

2. is a **dutiful** employee ______________

3. to **inspire** the youth by good example ______________

4. a public **homage** that made her proud ______________

5. asked to **trudge** across the stage ______________

Completing the Sentence

From the words in this unit, choose the one that best completes each of the following sentences. Write the word in the space provided.

1. Such capacity for growth and self-improvement can be expected only in the ______________ years of the teens and early twenties.

2. How could they have ______________ themselves by joining in that obscene celebration?

3. Instead of settling down to a job and a family, Tom seems to be modeling his life on the career of some rogue out of a(n) ______________ novel.

4. Should we expect the needs and purposes of a true poet to be understood by such a thoroughgoing ______________?

5. Oscar's careless housekeeping and sloppy habits were an endless source of exasperation to his ______________ roommate.

6. As we turned in to the ranch, we saw two young foals ______________ playfully in the open field.

7. You made some rather clever suggestions at the meeting, but on the whole, your ideas were far too ______________ to serve as the basis for a workable plan.

8. The purpose of the course in American history is to ______________ young people with a genuine understanding of what this country stands for.

9. They showed such a deplorable lack of ______________ in handling that difficult situation that they converted a mere unpleasantness into a social disaster.

10. I freely confess that just the sight of a roller coaster is enough to make me feel ______________.

11. Perhaps once in a generation, a people is faced with a great moral crisis in which it must ____________________ for good or evil, war or peace, life or death.

12. The young pianist dazzled the audience with the ____________________ and verve of his performance.

13. The entire issue of the magazine was designed as a(n) ____________________ satirizing the follies and futilities of mass-consumption advertising.

14. I was confident that I would do well in the scholarship examination, but my hopes were dashed by my old ____________________, mathematics.

15. Because I had unlimited faith in their honesty and discretion, I felt no qualms about giving them ____________________ to do whatever they thought was necessary.

16. A host of creditors ____________________ the hapless businessman with demands for payment and threats of legal action.

17. Though Jane's mount was as docile as a newborn lamb, mine proved to be the most ____________________ animal I had ever ridden.

18. There are circumstances under which it is desirable to make decisions swiftly and unequivocally, but there are other cases in which it is wise to hold decisions in ____________________.

19. Her equivocal answers to my questions about going to college in the fall clearly revealed her ____________________ attitude toward leaving home.

20. Many scientists are fearful that the West Coast may someday suffer a(n) ____________________ as violent as the earthquake that devastated San Francisco in 1906.

Writing: Words in Action

1. Look back at "On the Edge" (pages 88–89). Consider the risks and the thrill of kayaking or canoeing in white water, and then consider at least two other extreme sports. Write a descriptive essay that discusses the risks and the thrills of these sports. Use at least three details from the passage and three unit words.

2. Imagine you are one of the friends mentioned in the "On the Edge" narrative (pages 88–89). Write a letter or e-mail to the narrator in which you convince her to go kayaking for the first time. Write at least three paragraphs and use three or more words from this unit.

Vocabulary in Context

Literary Text

The following excerpts are from Somerset Maugham's novels Of Human Bondage, The Explorer, *and* The Moon and Sixpence. *Some of the words you have studied in this unit appear in* ***boldface*** *type. Complete each statement below the excerpt by circling the letter of the correct answer.*

1. "Sally never pays any attention to me," laughed Athelny, looking at her with fond, proud eyes. "She goes about her business indifferent to wars, revolutions, and **cataclysms**. What a wife she'll make to an honest man!" (*Of Human Bondage*)

A **cataclysm** is a

a. disaster
b. breakthrough
c. détente
d. disease

2. He was **fastidious**, and, aiming at something he did not quite fully grasp, was constantly dissatisfied with his work as a whole: perhaps a part would please him, the forearm or the leg and foot of a figure, a glass or a cup in a still-life ... (*Of Human Bondage*)

Someone who is **fastidious** is NOT

a. conspicuous
b. punctilious
c. old
d. lax

3. First of all he meant to go to Spain. That was the land of his heart; and by now he was **imbued** with its spirit, its romance and color and history and grandeur; he felt that it had a message for him in particular which no other country could give. (*Of Human Bondage*)

To be **imbued** with something is to be

a. pervaded by it
b. renewed by it
c. disgusted by it
d. unsettled by it

Leslie Howard and Bette Davis star in the 1934 film adaptation of *Of Human Bondage.*

4. Lucy, though very fond of him, was mildly scornful of his **philistine** outlook. He cared nothing for books, and the only form of art that appealed to him was the musical comedy. (*The Explorer*)

A **philistine** is someone who does not care for

a. material things
b. people
c. the arts
d. sports

5. He must have acquired experiences which would form abundant material for a **picaresque** novel of modern Paris, but he remained aloof, and judging from his conversation there was nothing in those years that had made a particular impression on him. (*The Moon and Sixpence*)

A **picaresque** novel is a novel about a(n)

a. evil person
b. roguish hero
c. woman
d. elite person

Snap the code, or go to **vocabularyworkshop.com**

UNIT 8

*Read the following selection, taking note of the **boldface** words and their contexts. These words are among those you will be studying in Unit 8. As you complete the exercises in this unit, it may help to refer to the way the words are used below.*

Target This!

<Persuasive Essay>

Your laptop is in cahoots with companies to get you to buy stuff. Think the idea is farfetched or something out of a dystopian novel? Think again. It's no **aberration**. When you click on a popular website or click to a new link, that information is captured by sophisticated tracking software that sends data to businesses or organizations eager to sign you up as a customer, client, or member. And it's not just when you use your desktop computer: More and more online marketers are using apps to track and collect data from smartphone users. This practice is called targeted advertising, or behavioral targeting, and it's a multibillion-dollar industry that's growing fast. E-commerce is booming, and experts say online tracking technology is only the beginning, a **harbinger** of things to come. Is this form of niche marketing a **de facto** deception and a **depredation**—or a forward-thinking way to help you discover the goods and services that might interest you?

Accept cookies

Online retailers are tracking consumers in order to pinpoint and engage potential customers, get an e-edge, and boost **lackluster** sales. Advertisers use "cookies" to keep track of your browsing and shopping habits, tastes, preferences, and behaviors and then display ads that correspond to your past clicks or purchases; social-networking sites collect user actions in the form of comments, clicks, and profile updates. The newest technologies are able to predict, often to an uncanny degree of accuracy, what your next steps online might be. Customer profiles can include information like age, gender, race, income, marital status, and more. With this information, advertisers are able to drill down into niches and target subniches. They can use tracking information to create relevant advertisements and content that they think people might want to see, to **pander** to even the most unusual **peccadilloes** and whims of the consumer. Meanwhile, some online retailers are working to earn their customers' confidence and are taking steps to safeguard personal data. And some believe that the **pièce de résistance** is a seal of approval from a trusted third party, such as the Better Business Bureau, which has strict standards for bestowing accreditation. Marketers maintain that personal privacy isn't violated because Web site visitors aren't identified by name, but not everyone agrees with that assertion.

The amount of information gathered about unsuspecting consumers is frightening, and computer users need to know about it. While there is **empathy** for businesses needing to think creatively and create buzz for their brand, consumer concerns are increasing and are the **bane** of advertisers. The advice, "Let the buyer beware," is something every computer user should heed. Privacy-rights groups and opponents of targeted niche advertising aren't merely noisy **malcontents** forming **ad hoc** protests. They have plenty of powerful allies: Congress has stepped into the fray, with a few **cantankerous** lawmakers questioning online sellers' ethics and **casuistry** and pushing for more regulation and consumer protection. The issue has also been **remanded** to the Federal Trade Commission for review.

Are you willing to give up your privacy every time you access news, music, and entertainment sites? Do you want to hand over details of your life to a grasping retailer who will use your own data against you? Write to your congressperson to demand stricter Web-data-collecting regulations!

Snap the code, or go to **vocabularyworkshop.com**

Write a review

Definitions

Note the spelling, pronunciation, part(s) of speech, and definition(s) of each of the following words. Then write the word in the blank spaces in the illustrative sentence(s) following. Finally, study the lists of synonyms and antonyms.

1. aberration (ab ə rā′ shən)

(*n.*) a departure from what is proper, right, expected, or normal; a lapse from a sound mental state

In an ____________________ of judgment, the coach chose not to call a critical time-out.

SYNONYMS: deviation, irregularity

2. ad hoc (ad′ häk′)

(*adj.*) for this specific purpose; improvised; (*adv.*) with respect to this

An ____________________ committee was formed immediately.

We met, ____________________, to consider the issue.

SYNONYM: (*adj.*) makeshift
ANTONYM: (*adj.*) permanent, long-standing

3. bane (bān)

(*n.*) the source or cause of fatal injury, death, destruction, or ruin; death or ruin itself; poison

Rain, the ____________________ of picnics, was forecast for the day we had scheduled ours.

SYNONYMS: spoiler, bête noire
ANTONYMS: blessing, comfort, solace, balm

4. bathos (bā′ thos)

(*n.*) the intrusion of commonplace or trite material into a context whose tone is lofty or elevated; grossly insincere or exaggerated sentimentality; the lowest phase, nadir; an anticlimax, comedown

After wallowing in ____________________, the writer returned to her novel in earnest.

SYNONYMS: mawkishness, mush

5. cantankerous (kan taŋ′ kə rəs)

(*adj.*) ill-tempered, quarrelsome; difficult to get along or deal with

The ____________________ machine befuddled the team of technicians assigned to repair it.

SYNONYMS: cranky, testy, peevish, irascible, ornery
ANTONYMS: good-natured, sweet-tempered, genial

6. casuistry (kazh′ ū is trē)

(*n.*) the determination of right and wrong in questions of conduct or conscience by the application of general ethical principles; specious argument

The professor's ideas, once highly regarded, now appear to be nothing more than ingenious ____________________.

SYNONYM: quibbling

7. de facto
(dē fak′ tō)

(*adj.*) actually existing or in effect, although not legally required or sanctioned; (*adv.*) in reality, actually

The dictator's wife is the ______________________ head of state.

It appears that, ______________________, the information is true.

SYNONYMS: in actuality, in point of fact
ANTONYMS: de jure, by right

8. depredation
(dep rə dā′ shən)

(*n.*) the act of preying upon or plundering

The ______________________ of the invaders left scars that will take years to heal.

SYNONYMS: looting, outrage

9. empathy
(em′ pə thē)

(*n.*) a sympathetic understanding of or identification with the feelings, thoughts, or attitudes of someone or something else

The grandparents felt ______________________ for the aspirations of their grandchildren.

SYNONYMS: sympathy, compassion
ANTONYMS: insensitivity, callousness, detachment

10. harbinger
(här′ bən jər)

(*n.*) a forerunner, herald; (*v.*) to herald the approach of

Daffodils in bloom are a ______________________ of spring.

Crocuses, too, ______________________ the approach of spring.

SYNONYMS: (*n.*) precursor; (*v.*) presage
ANTONYMS: (*n.*) aftermath, epilogue, sequel

11. hedonism
(hē′ də niz əm)

(*n.*) the belief that the attainment of pleasure is life's chief aim; devotion to or pursuit of pleasure

A beach bum's mindless ______________________ may appeal to all working people at one time or another.

SYNONYMS: pleasure seeking, sensuality
ANTONYMS: asceticism, puritanism

12. lackluster
(lak′ lus tər)

(*adj.*) lacking brilliance or vitality; dull

The weary soldier's ______________________ stare haunted the photographer, who captured it with her lens.

SYNONYMS: vapid, insipid, drab, flat
ANTONYMS: brilliant, radiant, dazzling

13. malcontent
(mal′ kən tent)

(*adj.*) discontented with or in open defiance of prevailing conditions; (*n.*) such a person

The ______________________ transit workers went out on strike.

The angry mayor referred to the strikers as a group of vocal, lazy ____________________.

SYNONYMS: (*adj.*) dissatisfied, disgruntled; (*n.*) grumbler
ANTONYMS: (*adj.*) satisfied, contented, complacent, smug

14. mellifluous (mə lif′ lü əs)

(*adj.*) flowing sweetly or smoothly; honeyed

The folk singer's ____________________ voice appealed to young and old the world over.

SYNONYM: euphonious; ANTONYMS: strident, harsh, grating

15. nepotism (nep′ ə tiz əm)

(*n.*) undue favoritism to or excessive patronage of one's relatives

To avoid any hint of ____________________, the owner of the team refused to hire any of his relatives.

16. pander (pan′ dər)

(*v.*) to cater to or provide satisfaction for the low tastes or vices of others; (*n.*) a person who does this

The hosts proceeded to ____________________ to every whim of their delighted guests.

His brother was a ____________________ who ran a cheap pool hall on the outskirts of town.

SYNONYMS: (*v.*) indulge; (*n.*) pimp, procurer

17. peccadillo (pek ə dil′ ō)

(*n.*) a minor sin or offense; a trifling fault or shortcoming

If you will overlook my ____________________, I will ignore yours.

SYNONYM: lapse; ANTONYMS: felony, mortal sin, enormity, atrocity

18. pièce de résistance (pē əs də rā zē stäns′)

(*n.*) the principal dish of a meal; the principal event, incident, or item; an outstanding accomplishment

The ____________________ of the remarkable repast was the dessert, a ten-tiered cake adorned with spun sugar.

SYNONYMS: centerpiece, chef d'oeuvre
ANTONYMS: preliminary, hors d'oeuvre

19. remand (ri mand′)

(*v.*) to send or order back; in law, to send back to jail or to a lower court

The outlaw was ____________________ to the custody of the sheriff.

SYNONYMS: remit, return; ANTONYMS: forward to, send on, release

20. syndrome (sin′ drōm)

(*n.*) a group of symptoms or signs that collectively characterizes or indicates a disease, disorder, abnormality, etc.

With ubiquitous computer use, carpal tunnel has become a decidedly modern ____________________.

SYNONYMS: complex, pattern

Choosing the Right Word

*Select the **boldface** word that better completes each sentence. You might refer to the selection on pages 98–99 to see how most of these words are used in context.*

1. So strong is my (**empathy, casuistry**) with the poems of Robert Frost that I often feel as though I could have written them myself.

2. Although the law forbids residential separation of the races, we all know that a state of (**de facto, ad hoc**) segregation exists in some communities.

3. How can you compare a mere social (**peccadillo, depredation**) with a misdeed that has caused such great harm to other people?

4. We may find (**malcontents, hedonists**) annoying, but the fact is that they often serve as "gadflies" to bring about desirable changes.

The American poet Robert Frost (1874–1963) wrote verse about ordinary people and was awarded the Pulitzer Prize.

5. The (**baneful, mellifluous**) looks that they directed at us made it only too clear that we had little hope for mercy at their hands.

6. We must not assume that their behavior, however (**aberrant, mellifluous**) by conventional standards, is a sign of mental illness.

7. Then came Miss Bolton's cornet solo, which we all recognized immediately as the (**pièce de résistance, casuistry**) of that long musical evening.

8. The car was forever breaking down, but its owner seemed to derive a sort of perverse satisfaction out of battling with the (**mellifluous, cantankerous**) old heap.

9. Said Churchill to the British people after the Munich agreement: "We must reject these (**mellifluous, malcontent**) assurances of 'peace in our time.'"

10. In all aspects of their behavior, Raina and Joe showed the self-indulgence and gross indifference to others that is characteristic of the true (**malcontent, hedonist**).

11. The (**syndrome, bathos**) of poverty, drug addiction, and crime that afflicts our cities calls for remedial action on a truly national scale.

12. The (**aberrations, depredations**) of the terrible disease could be seen only too clearly in her extreme emaciation and feebleness.

13. A candidate for high public office should seek to debate the issues on an objective level, instead of (**remanding, pandering**) to the prejudices of the times.

14. "Am I to be accused of (**casuistry, nepotism**)," queried the Mayor, "just because my wife, daughter, brother, and nephew happen to be the best applicants for the jobs?"

15. True, we won the game, but I think our team gave a rather (**lackluster, malcontent**) performance in beating a weak opponent by so narrow a margin.

16. In many respects it is a good movie, but sadly, the director has allowed sentiment to spill over into sentimentality, and sentimentality into (**bathos, casuistry**).

17. Your efforts to prove that because "no one is perfect," all moral standards are relative and therefore meaningless, struck me as sheer (**casuistry, hedonism**).

18. The negotiators agreed not to try to draw up an overall treaty but to deal with each specific problem on a(n) (**de facto, ad hoc**) basis.

19. With the extreme cold and the deep snows still holding on, the gradual lengthening of the days was the only (**aberration, harbinger**) of spring.

20. We learned with dismay that our application had been neither approved nor rejected, but (**pandered, remanded**) to a "higher authority for further consideration."

21. Our fundraising committee formed (**de facto, ad hoc**) in order to more efficiently help the displaced or uninsured families that were affected by the floods.

22. Since you've been spending time with these new friends, I sense in you a sort of mental (**bane, aberration**) that both worries and disappoints me.

23. The (**mellifluous, malcontent**) citizens formed a committee to disseminate a petition, to organize a general strike, and to monitor legislative proceedings.

24. The movement of the red fox north into arctic fox territory (**harbingers, remands**) the continuation of a warming climate.

25. The man in the gray cap is a (**pander, bane**) who engages in all kinds of illegal activities but somehow never gets caught.

Synonyms

*Choose the word from this unit that is the same or most nearly the same in meaning as the **boldface** word or expression in the phrase. Write that word on the line. Use a dictionary if necessary.*

1. **sybaritism** that is indulged in Las Vegas ______________
2. is a **herald** of the coming of winter ______________
3. struck me as utter **sophistry** ______________
4. victims of the **pillage** ______________
5. dismissed as **schmaltz** by critics ______________
6. seen by scientists as an **anomaly** ______________
7. committed several **indiscretions** ______________
8. the **musical** tone of the announcer's voice ______________
9. charged with **favoritism** by his opponents ______________
10. suffers from a recognizable **group of symptoms** ______________

Antonyms

*Choose the word from this unit that is most nearly opposite in meaning to the **boldface** word or expression in the phrase. Write that word on the line. Use a dictionary if necessary.*

1. the **sublimity** of the story's conclusion ______________________
2. never experienced **self-denial** ______________________
3. awakened by the **shrill** sound ______________________
4. the **isolated side effect** caused by the medicine ______________________
5. the refreshing **impartiality** of the manager ______________________

Completing the Sentence

From the words in this unit, choose the one that best completes each of the following sentences. Write the word in the space provided.

1. Would it be ungracious of me to suggest that the ______________________ of the feast, given on the menu as "filet mignon," had the taste and texture of old shoe leather?
2. It took years for that country to recover from the ______________________ wrought by the Second World War and its concomitant social and economic dislocations.
3. The history of the world teaches us that we should never let ourselves be blinded by the meretricious ______________________ of a demagogue, no matter how appealing it may appear at first glance.
4. I find myself in the position of ______________________ supervisor; now I would like to have the title, salary, and privileges that go along with the job.
5. Yes, you have scored a quick commercial success, but you have done it only by ______________________ to low and depraved tastes.
6. Those sentimentalized effusions introduced a note of ______________________ into what should have been an occasion marked by dignity and restraint.
7. Is it too optimistic to hope that your willingness to undertake that thankless task is the ______________________ of a new maturity and a more responsible attitude?
8. Though he had embraced a creed of unabashed ______________________ in his youth, he ended his life among a group of ascetics living in the desert.
9. Because they have followed a policy of bringing in executives and supervisors from the outside, instead of promoting from within their own ranks, the office is filled with grumbling ______________________.
10. Yes, I believe in helping out relatives, but I haven't spent a lifetime building this business to make it a monument to ______________________.

11. The pitcher's lightning fastball has proved the ____________________ of many a celebrated home-run hitter.

12. A high temperature, yellowish complexion, and general feeling of fatigue are all characteristic of the mononucleosis ____________________.

13. He had been happy-go-lucky as a young man, but years of disappointment and misfortune have turned him sour and ____________________.

14. It was hard to believe that the eager, vibrant youth I had known was now this shabby derelict, staring into space with ____________________ eyes.

15. Those cases that call for further attention will be ____________________ to the proper agencies.

16. As there was no agency concerned with race relations, the Mayor created a(n) ____________________ committee to deal with such matters.

17. I think you are showing poor judgment in condemning them so severely for what is, after all, little more than a(n) ____________________.

18. How is one to explain that strange ____________________ from the habits and standards that he had followed for so many years?

19. Like everyone else, I was charmed by the ____________________ tones of the speaker, but later I could extract very little real meaning from what she had said.

20. Her visits to the nursing home are motivated not by a detached sense of duty but by a genuine ____________________ for those who are lonely.

Writing: Words in Action

1. Look back at "Target This!" (pages 98–99). Consider the e-marketing and business practices common among online retailers nowadays, and then consider what these businesses may or may not know about you. Write an essay in which you write a definition of "personal privacy" and describe how it has, or hasn't, changed over the past 50 to 100 years. Use at least three details from the passage and three unit words.

2. At the end of "Target This!" the writer asks, "Are you willing to give up your privacy every time you access news, music, and entertainment sites?" In a brief essay, write your own answer to this question with specific examples from your studies, reading (refer to pages 98–99), or personal observations and experience. Write at least three paragraphs and use three or more words from this unit.

Vocabulary in Context

Literary Text

*The following excerpts are from works by Sir Arthur Conan Doyle. Some of the words you have studied in this unit appear in **boldface** type. Complete each statement below the excerpt by circling the letter of the correct answer.*

1. Mr. Lestrade . . . and Mr. Sherlock Holmes . . . have each come to the conclusion that the grotesque series of incidents, which have ended in so tragic a fashion, arise from lunacy rather than from deliberate crime. No explanation save mental **aberration** can cover the facts. (*The Return of Sherlock Holmes*)

An **aberration** is a(n)

a. plundering
b. irregularity
c. poison
d. argument

2. The temptation to form premature theories upon insufficient data is the **bane** of our profession. I can see only two things for certain at present—a great brain in London, and a dead man in Sussex. (*The Valley of Fear*)

A **bane** is a(n)

a. embarrassment
b. accomplishment
c. nadir
d. tribulation

Eddie Marsan appears as Inspector Lestrade in the 2009 film *Sherlock Holmes,* directed by Guy Ritchie.

3. As a Pressman, I felt sure from what I had been told that I could never hope to get into touch with this **cantankerous** Professor. (*The Lost World*)

Someone who is **cantankerous** is NOT

a. amiable
b. repugnant
c. grumpy
d. saturnalian

4. A large section of the audience expressed their indignation at such a slur upon the travelers by noisy shouts of dissent and cries of, "Don't put it!" "Withdraw!" "Turn him out!" On the other hand, the **malcontents**—and it cannot be denied that they were fairly numerous—cheered for the amendment . . . (*The Lost World*)

A **malcontent** is a

a. simpleton
b. benefactor
c. scoundrel
d. troublemaker

5. "I called about that beggarman, Boone—the one who was charged with being concerned in the disappearance of Mr. Neville St. Clair, of Lee."

"Yes. He was brought up and **remanded** for further inquiries." (*The Adventures of Sherlock Holmes*)

To be **remanded** is to be

a. protected
b. maligned
c. detained
d. scolded

Snap the code, or go to **vocabularyworkshop.com**

UNIT 9

Read the following selection, taking note of the ***boldface*** *words and their contexts. These words are among those you will be studying in Unit 9. As you complete the exercises in this unit, it may help to refer to the way the words are used below.*

Volunteer Profile: Jennifer Yoder

<Profile>

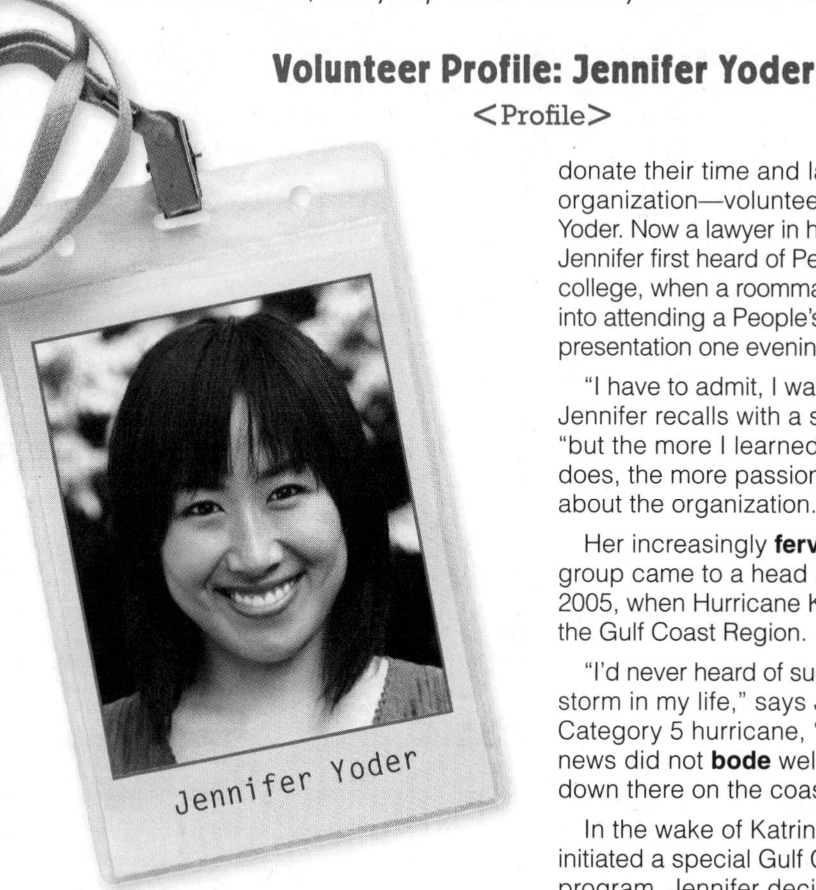

In the 40 years since its foundation, the nonprofit organization People's Habitat has worked to eliminate poverty-housing and homelessness from the world and to make decent housing a matter of conscience and action. The organization's efforts are **ecumenical** in scope, with active programs across the globe. People's Habitat has provided over 450,000 affordable homes and served over 2,100,000 people to date, earning **kudos** from presidents, community leaders, and activists alike.

People's Habitat could not function without the thousands of volunteers who donate their time and labor to the organization—volunteers like Jennifer Yoder. Now a lawyer in her early thirties, Jennifer first heard of People's Habitat in college, when a roommate **inveigled** her into attending a People's slide show presentation one evening.

"I have to admit, I was reluctant at first," Jennifer recalls with a sheepish laugh, "but the more I learned about what PH does, the more passionate I became about the organization."

Her increasingly **fervid** interest in the group came to a head in the summer of 2005, when Hurricane Katrina devastated the Gulf Coast Region.

"I'd never heard of such a **gargantuan** storm in my life," says Jennifer of the Category 5 hurricane, "and the early news did not **bode** well for the people down there on the coast."

In the wake of Katrina, PH quickly initiated a special Gulf Coast Emergency program. Jennifer decided to take a semester off from law school and pitch in.

"Everywhere I looked," she explained, "I saw damaged property and battered **infrastructure**. Most of the houses left standing in coastal Mississippi were rotten, full of mold and **dank**, **fetid** air."

People's Habitat shipped pre-constructed housing components to the region, assembled them in areas less stricken by the storm, and installed them at recovery sites in record time. The rapid progress gave many residents the strength not to **truckle** to despair, so often a **bête noire** for disaster victims.

"Gulf Coast Emergency was the **heyday** of my participation with People's Habitat," beams Jennifer, "and I really gained so much from the experience. I don't mean to sound like a **sycophant**, but with People's Habitat you really do give a little to get a lot."

A lot has changed for Jennifer in the years since Gulf Coast Emergency. She graduated from law school and currently works for a medium-sized law firm in her hometown of Akron, Ohio.

"Most of my volunteer work is spent behind a desk lately, and on the phone," she confesses, "because I mainly focus on fundraising nowadays."

Asked if she misses getting her hands dirty, Jennifer laughs.

"Sure I do. The memory of working together with all those volunteers and family members to build homes, it brings up such a positive feeling, like a deep sense of **beatitude**."

Fortunately, it sounds as if Jennifer will soon be back building houses. She's promised her niece and **protégé**, Tula, that they'll work together on a local Women Construct project nearby in Summit County before Tula heads off to college next fall. PH's Women Construct projects typically involve an all-female crew of construction volunteers, with men invited to participate as onsite assistants and teachers.

"Tula's been talking about it all year, and I'm pretty excited about it myself. We'll have an opportunity to help a hard-working family in need—and it'll be a great bonding experience too!"

Women volunteers help build homes for the needy.

Flooded homes in New Orleans, September 2005

Definitions

Note the spelling, pronunciation, part(s) of speech, and definition(s) of each of the following words. Then write the word in the blank spaces in the illustrative sentence(s) following. Finally, study the lists of synonyms and antonyms.

1. avatar
(a′ və tär)

(*n.*) an embodiment (as of a concept or philosophy) often in a person; an electronic image that represents and is manipulated by a computer user

Once users choose ____________________ for the application, they can select preferences and virtually connect with friends.

SYNONYMS: embodiment, virtual identity

2. beatitude
(bē at′ ə tüd)

(*n.*) a state of perfect happiness or blessedness; a blessing

Do you think that not having to worry about money is the consummate ____________________ of being wealthy?

SYNONYMS: bliss, rapture
ANTONYMS: misery, despair

3. bête noire
(bet nwär′)

(*n.*) someone or something that one especially dislikes, dreads, or avoids

Spinach used to be the ____________________ of my diet, but that was before I tasted blood sausage.

SYNONYMS: pet peeve, bugbear, nemesis
ANTONYMS: pet, idol

4. bode
(bōd)

(*v.*) to be an omen of; to indicate by signs

With a smile that ____________________ well, the teacher enters the room and greets the students.

SYNONYMS: presage, augur, foreshadow

5. dank
(daŋk)

(*adj.*) unpleasantly damp or wet

The room had the ____________________ atmosphere of a wet cave.

SYNONYMS: clammy, moist, soggy
ANTONYMS: dry, arid, parched, desiccated

6. ecumenical
(ek yu men′ i kəl)

(*adj.*) worldwide or universal in influence or application

An ____________________ council meets on the third Tuesday of each month.

SYNONYMS: general, comprehensive
ANTONYMS: parochial, regional, insular

7. fervid
(fər′ vid)

(*adj.*) burning with enthusiasm or zeal; extremely heated

Using ____________________ words of praise, the coach gave the team a much-needed pep talk before the big game.

SYNONYMS: ardent, fervent, earnest
ANTONYMS: apathetic, indifferent, cool, blasé

8. fetid
(fet′ id)

(*adj.*) having an unpleasant or offensive odor

The stale, ____________________ air of the windowless room was an irritation to all who had to be there.

SYNONYMS: smelly, putrid, noisome, foul, malodorous
ANTONYMS: fragrant, aromatic, perfumed, sweet

9. gargantuan
(gär gan′ chū ən)

(*adj.*) of immense size, volume, or capacity; enormous, prodigious

The spirited artist had a ____________________ thirst for life.

SYNONYMS: huge, colossal, mammoth, gigantic
ANTONYMS: tiny, minuscule, infinitesimal, dwarfish

10. heyday
(hā′ dā)

(*n.*) the period of greatest power, vigor, success, or influence; the prime years

During the ____________________ of the clipper ship, these graceful vessels were the swiftest on the seas.

SYNONYM: golden age
ANTONYMS: formative years, twilight years, decline

11. incubus
(iŋ′ kyə bəs)

(*n.*) a demon or evil spirit supposed to haunt human beings in their bedrooms at night; anything that oppresses or weighs upon one, like a nightmare

The young child awoke with a loud scream, claiming that a terrifying ____________________ had entered the room.

SYNONYMS: hobgoblin, millstone

12. infrastructure
(in′ frə strək chər)

(*n.*) a basic foundation or framework; a system of public works; the resources and facilities required for an activity; permanent military installations

The city's aging ____________________ was beginning to become a problem that needed to be addressed.

SYNONYMS: base, basis, underpinning
ANTONYM: superstructure

13. inveigle
(in vā′ gəl)

(*v.*) to entice, lure, or snare by flattery or artful inducements; to obtain or acquire by artifice

The planning committee chair ____________________ us to join them by promising good seats at the ceremony.

SYNONYMS: induce, beguile, cajole, wheedle

14. kudos
(kü′ dōs)

(*n.*) the acclaim, prestige, or renown that comes as a result of some action or achievement

The poet received all the ____________________ due a Nobel laureate.

SYNONYMS: glory, praise, accolades
ANTONYMS: boos, disapproval, condemnation

15. lagniappe
(lan′ yap)

(*n.*) an extra or unexpected gift or gratuity

To reward their loyal customers, the grateful store handed out ____________________ to all the day's shoppers.

SYNONYM: bonus

16. prolix
(prō lix′)

(*adj.*) long-winded and wordy; tending to speak or write in such a way

The father of the bride regaled anyone who would listen with a ____________________ description of the wedding.

SYNONYM: garrulous
ANTONYMS: laconic, succinct, pithy

17. protégé
(prō′ tə zhā)

(*n.*) someone whose welfare, training, or career is under the patronage of an influential person; someone under the jurisdiction of a foreign country or government

The ____________________ of the ex-champion may one day be a champion herself.

SYNONYMS: ward, charge, disciple, trainee
ANTONYMS: sponsor, mentor, benefactor

18. sycophant
(sik′ ə fənt)

(*n.*) someone who attempts to win favors or advance him- or herself by flattery or servile behavior; a slanderer, defamer

The actor, angered by his manager's constant false flattery, called him a two-faced ____________________.

SYNONYMS: yes-man, flunky, bootlicker

19. tautology
(tô tol′ ə jē)

(*n.*) needless repetition of an idea by using different but equivalent words; a redundancy

Filled with endless ____________________ and solecisms, the lengthy book is a tiresome read.

SYNONYM: pleonasm

20. truckle
(truk′ əl)

(*v.*) to yield or submit tamely or submissively

The knight would ____________________ to no one.

SYNONYMS: kowtow, stoop, grovel
ANTONYMS: resist, defy, stand up to

Choosing the Right Word

*Select the **boldface** word that better completes each sentence. You might refer to the selection on pages 108–109 to see how most of these words are used in context.*

This sculpture of the Hindu god Vishnu shows a four-handed version of the god.

1. The Hindu god Vishnu is most often associated with ten (**avatars, sycophants**), while the god also has about 10,000 names.
2. In all the great philosophies, we find common standards that must be regarded as (**fervid, ecumenical**) values, equally valid at all times and in all places.
3. Our goal as a nation and as a society must be to free ourselves completely of the (**sycophant, incubus**) of racial prejudice.
4. Surely you can make an honest effort to please your employer without (**boding, truckling**) to the vanity of the person who pays your salary.
5. You did nothing to help me, but now that I have achieved some success, you have the gall to claim me as your (**protégé, bête noire**).
6. We can now recognize that many institutions that seemed, at a particular time, to be in their (**incubus, heyday**) were actually already on the decline.
7. When I saw the beautiful girl you had brought to the prom, I understood the reason for your smile of (**fetid, beatific**) self-satisfaction.
8. The lowering clouds and mounting winds did not (**bode, truckle**) well for our hopes for perfect beach weather.
9. I have no desire to be known as a nonconformist, but I am not going to allow fear of public disapproval to become my (**beatitude, bête noire**).
10. My criticism of his statement is not merely that it is (**prolix, ecumenical**), but that it uses words to obscure rather than to reinforce the meaning.
11. The emergency room nurse is the very (**avatar, lagniappe**) of patience and generosity, as he or she often stays at the hospital late to comfort patients.
12. His zest for life and his boundless optimism were expressed perfectly, it seemed to me, in his (**gargantuan, fetid**) smile.
13. In the twilight of her long career, she began to receive the (**heyday, kudos**) that her brilliant but unconventional writings so richly deserved.
14. Her composition was seriously weakened by (**tautologies, kudos**) such as "an older woman who is approaching the end of her life span."
15. Scientists have for some time been correlating the functions of human consciousness with the neural (**tautology, infrastructure**) of the brain.

16. The corporate (**sycophant, bête noire**) did succeed in climbing the ladder of success for a few years, but his repellent behavior eventually caught up with him.

17. I was paid generously for my work, but the kind smile and gracious words were a delightful (**lagniappe, incubus**).

18. I felt that I could not continue to live any longer in that (**dank, gargantuan**) atmosphere of prejudice and hostility.

19. She was such a (**beatific, fervid**) supporter of the Los Angeles Dodgers that she seemed unable to speak of anything else.

20. When the sanitation strike continued into a second week, people began to complain about the (**fetid, prolix**) smell that hung over the sweltering city.

21. After a long investigation, detectives arrested two con artists who had (**truckled, inveigled**) many elderly victims into giving the con artists their life savings.

22. The crashing thunder and piercing lightning seemed to summon a(n) (**beatitude, incubus**) that haunted the child in her sleep.

23. Surrounded from childhood by flattering courtiers, the monarch grew to adulthood unable to distinguish a friend from a (**beatitude, sycophant**).

24. The reporter (**inveigled, truckled**) herself into the private courtroom proceedings by convincing the bailiff that she was his childhood friend.

25. To choose giving over receiving is to reap eternal (**lagniappe, beatitude**).

Synonyms

*Choose the word from this unit that is the same or most nearly the same in meaning as the **boldface** word or expression in the phrase. Write that word on the line. Use a dictionary if necessary.*

1. the **burden** of famine and disease ____________________
2. abounds in **redundancy** ____________________
3. is a **zealous** follower of the guru ____________________
4. a tottering **foundation** ____________________
5. a **verbose** essay impresses no one ____________________
6. known throughout the town as a **toady** ____________________
7. a document of **worldwide** significance ____________________
8. an unexpected **gratuity** ____________________
9. a great champion in her **prime** ____________________
10. the very **manifestation** of conservatism ____________________

Antonyms

*Choose the word from this unit that is most nearly opposite in meaning to the **boldface** word or expression in the phrase. Write that word on the line. Use a dictionary if necessary.*

1. a **computer user** manipulates the mouse ____________
2. wrote a **terse** passage ____________
3. **penalty** for returning the book late ____________
4. imaginary and inspiring **muse** ____________
5. a carefully constructed and **concise statement** ____________

Completing the Sentence

From the words in this unit, choose the one that best completes each of the following sentences. Write the word in the space provided.

1. Falstaff is a behemoth personality, whose ____________ appetites, especially for sack and sleep, never seem to be satiated.

2. Once I created an inexact ____________ for the new dancing video game, I became inexplicably motivated to exercise.

3. After I read one of your ____________ and repetitive reports, I always have the feeling that you have never heard the expression "less is more."

4. I think it was terribly naive of us to expect to get a fair hearing from such ____________ partisans of the opposing party.

5. It was a subject of heated debate in the early nineteenth century whether the federal government should play any part at all in building the ____________ to support the fledgling American economy.

6. Was it just our imagination, or was the room still ____________ with the smell of stale cigar smoke?

7. I was happy enough when she agreed to go to the prom with me, but her suggestion that we use her car was an unexpected ____________.

8. The atmosphere of mistrust and hostility did not ____________ well for the outcome of the peace talks.

9. In *David Copperfield*, Dickens described with heartbreaking realism the period of his own childhood that he spent toiling in a(n)____________ cellar.

10. At the risk of losing the election, I refused to ____________ to the fleeting passions and prejudices of a small part of the electorate.

11. The lame-duck president looked back with nostalgia on the power he had wielded during the ____________________ of his administration.

12. To maintain that, because human beings are aggressive animals, they will always be involved in conflicts seems to me a mere ____________________.

13. May I say, in all modesty, that I don't deserve such ____________________ just because I was all-state in football and led my class academically.

14. I consider the vogue use of "hopefully" illogical, inept, and pretentious; it has become my linguistic ____________________.

15. Far better to receive sincere criticism, no matter how severe, than to endure the groveling adulation of a(n) ____________________.

16. The speaker emphasized that in the modern world the barriers between different groups are rapidly being broken down and that we must try to think in truly ____________________ terms.

17. In the dreamy ____________________ of their first love, nothing I might have said would have had the slightest effect on them.

18. Like most people, I enjoy flattery, but I can't be ____________________ into doing something that in my heart I know is wrong.

19. The memory of my ghastly blunder and of the harm it had done to innocent people weighed on my spirit like a(n) ____________________.

20. As the ____________________ of one of the great violinists of our times, she has had an unrivaled opportunity to develop her musical talents.

Writing: Words in Action

1. Look back at "Volunteer Profile: Jennifer Yoder" (pages 108–109). Suppose you have just returned from a two-week trip working with People's Habitat, and you want to convince a friend or family member to go with you next time. Write an argument, using at least three details from the passage and three unit words, that might help you convince someone to volunteer for the organization.

2. *"Charity gives itself rich; covetousness hoards itself poor."—German proverb*

Do you think this saying remains true today? In a brief essay, explain what you think the proverb means, and then explain your opinion of its truth—or falseness—with specific examples from your studies, reading (refer to pages 108–109), or personal observations and experience. Write at least three paragraphs, and use three or more words from this unit.

Vocabulary in Context

Literary Text

*The following excerpts are from works by Wilkie Collins. Some of the words you have studied in this unit appear in **boldface** type. Complete each statement below the excerpt by circling the letter of the correct answer.*

1. But her looks and tones, when she spoke, were of a kind to make me more than serious—they distressed me. Her words, few as they were, betrayed a desperate clinging to the past which **boded** ill for the future. (*The Woman in White*)

If something **bodes** ill, it

a. reminds
b. warns
c. appeases
d. entices

2. Arnold repeated his answer to Sir Patrick, with **fervid** embellishments of the original language, suitable to the emergency. Blanche's delight expressed itself in the form of two unblushing outrages on propriety, committed in close succession. (*Man and Wife*)

To be **fervid** is to be

a. passionate
b. merry
c. outrageous
d. wrathful

In Wilkie Collins's *The Moonstone* (1868), Rachel Verinder confronts Franklin Blake.

3. Through all the hardening influences of the woman's life—through the fortifications against good which watchful evil builds in human hearts—that innocent outburst of trust and grief had broken its way; and had purified for a while the **fetid** inner darkness with divine light. (*Heart and Science*)

When something is **fetid**, it is NOT

a. confused
b. pungent
c. acrid
d. aromatic

4. I could write pages of affectionate warning on this one theme, but (alas!) I am not permitted to improve—I am condemned to narrate. My wealthy relative's check—henceforth, the **incubus** of my existence—warns me that I have not done with this record of violence yet. (*The Moonstone*)

An **incubus** causes

a. enlightenment
b. catastrophe
c. distress
d. bliss

5. The second of Mr. Sherwin's letters was much shorter than the first, and had apparently been written not more than a day or two back. His tone was changed; he **truckled** to me no longer—he began to threaten. (*Basil*)

To **truckle** is to

a. capitulate
b. compliment
c. condescend
d. criticize

Snap the code, or go to **vocabularyworkshop.com**

Vocabulary for Comprehension

*Read the following selection in which some of the words you have studied in Units 7–9 appear in **boldface** type. Then answer the questions on page 119.*

This passage describes ancient methods of waste disposal.

(Line)

In a list of the world's significant historical technological advances, one that surely deserves universal support for inclusion is the sewer. (5) **Kudos** to the ancient engineers who worked on the age-old problem of waste disposal. Imagine if they had not!

Today, an effective sewage system (10) is a key feature of the **infrastructure** of any city, large or small. But this was not always the case. One of the earliest attempts at a sewage system that improved upon the impractical (15) practice of hauling away waste and dumping it elsewhere took place about 5,000 years ago in the Orkney Islands, off the coast of Scotland. Archaeologists have discovered (20) evidence of stone-lined drains leading from small rooms in houses, going underground. These precursors of future sewers emptied into the sea through nearby cliffs.

(25) At about the same time, in the larger cities of the Indus Valley, engineers were dealing with the same issue, albeit on a grander scale. There, in what is now India (30) and Pakistan, they built networks of brick drains along the streets. Sewage ran from rooms in houses into underground U-shaped drains.

More than 2,000 years later, (35) sewage disposal methods had gained little in sophistication. For example, in the **heyday** of the great Athenian civilization, sewage pipes from houses emptied directly into (40) cesspools in the streets. Private contractors cleaned the foul mess.

Systems improved with the Romans, four centuries later. Emperor Augustus enclosed the (45) massive *Cloaca Maxima*, an enormous brick sewage tunnel that passed right through the center of the city. This structure, big enough for a chariot to pass through, was (50) one of many the Romans built throughout their empire. Never **ambivalent** about the importance of cleanliness, the Romans used their engineering skill to meet their (55) sanitation needs.

1. The main purpose of paragraph 1 (lines 1–8) is to
   a. create suspense
   b. share an interesting anecdote
   c. introduce the topic of the passage
   d. question why technological advances are often slow to develop
   e. question ancient engineers' talents

2. **Kudos** (line 5) most nearly means
   a. jobs
   b. profits
   c. boos
   d. accolades
   e. thanks

3. **Infrastructure** (line 10) means
   a. foundation
   b. government
   c. schools
   d. commerce
   e. superstructure

4. According to the writer, who found evidence for an ancient sewage system in the Orkney Islands?
   a. paleontologists
   b. engineers
   c. anthropologists
   d. geologists
   e. archaeologists

5. The main purpose of paragraph 2 (lines 9–24) is to
   a. describe one of the first sewage systems that was in the British Isles
   b. explain why ancient people wanted to build sewage systems
   c. persuade readers that the Scottish sewage system was the world's first
   d. pique reader interest and provide details of an unusual sewage system
   e. reveal recently discovered facts about ancient sewage systems

6. **Heyday** (line 37) most nearly means
   a. middle
   b. golden age
   c. beginning
   d. era
   e. declining years

7. Which best describes the organizational structure of the passage as a whole?
   a. chronological order
   b. cause and effect
   c. order of importance
   d. comparison and contrast
   e. spatial order

8. What was the Roman *Cloaca Maxima*?
   a. the leading guild of engineers
   b. the city's largest aqueduct
   c. the largest public square in the city
   d. the large brick sewage tunnel
   e. a broad Roman road

9. **Ambivalent** (line 52) is best defined as
   a. clear-cut
   b. compulsive
   c. serious
   d. meticulous
   e. equivocal

10. Which of the following best describes the author's tone in the passage?
    a. resigned
    b. incensed
    c. spirited
    d. melancholy
    e. objective

11. Which is a reasonable inference from details given in the passage?
    a. The Romans had better sewage disposal than the Athenians did.
    b. Indus Valley engineers were less imaginative than engineers in the Orkney Islands.
    c. The ancient Romans were indifferent to the importance of good hygiene.
    d. The Emperor Augustus possessed comparatively little foresight.
    e. Networks of brick drains were unnecessary in ancient Athens

12. According to the passage, Romans improved sewage systems about
    a. 1,500 years ago
    b. 2,500 years ago
    c. 3,500 years ago
    d. 4,000 years ago
    e. 5,000 years ago

Two-Word Completions

Select the pair of words that best complete the meaning of each of the following passages.

1. In the spring of that year, bands of marauding Goths broke into the province, ____________________ the governor in his own capital, and committed such ____________________ that the economy of the region did not recover for a generation.

a. beleaguered . . . depredations
b. lampooned . . . peccadillos
c. debauched . . . tautologies
d. remanded . . . abeyances

2. Miguel de Cervantes' *Don Quixote,* his magnificent and ____________________ novel, ____________________ just about every aspect of life—from the nobility to the common farmer—in sixteenth century Spain.

a. gamboled. . . ecumenical
b. remanded. . . gargantuan
c. picaresque. . . lampooned
d. truckled. . . lackluster

3. At the court of an autocratic ruler, free speech is usually replaced by the obsequious twaddle of self-seeking toadies and ____________________, eager to get ahead by ____________________ to the opinions of their all-powerful master.

a. lagniappes . . . debauching
b. sycophants . . . truckling
c. malcontents . . . lampooning
d. harbingers . . . pandering

4. Richard Wagner considered the average operagoer of his day a blatant ____________________, to whose benighted musical tastes he would in no way ____________________.

a. protégé . . . truckle
b. hedonist . . . remand
c. sycophant . . . opt
d. philistine . . . pander

5. In the ____________________ of network television in the United States, many people tuned in to watch police dramas or situation comedies; however, today's television is widely criticized for ____________________ its viewers with "reality" programming.

a. heyday . . . debauching
b. nepotism . . . boding
c. incubus . . . inveigling
d. carte blanche . . . truckling

6. David Bohm, an American physicist and ____________________ of Albert Einstein, has concluded that space and time are formulations of the human mind, and while some believe these ideas a(n) ____________________, he bases his hypotheses in science.

a. casuistry . . . beatitude
b. protégé . . . aberration
c. lagniappe . . . abeyance
d. nemesis . . . bathos

7. Our ____________________ and aging professor of history had his moments of brilliance, but so often had such a ____________________ presence in the classroom that students eventually learned to avoid his classes altogether.

a. ambivalent . . . malleable
b. ecumenical . . . fetid
c. cantankerous . . . lackluster
d. mellifluous . . . de facto

Proverbs

In the passage "Volunteer Profile: Jennifer Yoder" (see pages 108–109), the profiled People's Habitat volunteer restates the well-known proverb, "Give a little to get a lot."

This pithy statement is a **proverb**, or a short statement that expresses a general truth and includes a moral or a piece of advice. For example, the statement in the unit opener passage means that being generous, kind, or charitable brings great emotional reward as well satisfaction to both those who give of themselves and those who receive.

Choosing the Right Proverb

Read each sentence. Use context clues to figure out the meaning of each proverb in ***boldface*** *print. Then write the letter of the definition for the proverb in the sentence.*

1. When I couldn't decide what to study in college, my father said, "**Seek and ye shall find**." _______
2. When she admitted to stealing the T-shirt, her friend admonished her, "**Crime doesn't pay**." _______
3. If you think you are qualified for that job, apply right away! **He who hesitates is lost**. _______
4. I was told, "You can go to the pool after painting the shed. And remember: **Haste makes waste**." _______
5. Be careful. Don't sign up for too many classes or extracurricular activities this year. **Know thyself**. _______
6. **All's fair in love and war**. I will call the landlord every day until she refunds my security deposit. _______
7. She was unkind to you, but she wants to make amends. **To err is human; to forgive divine**. _______
8. You didn't reveal all that happened last night. Remember, **half the truth is often a whole lie**. _______
9. Stop fretting about whether or not you passed that class. **Cross that bridge when you come to it**. _______
10. Sure, she was pleased when her prank fooled me, but I have an even better prank planned. **He who laughs last laughs best**! _______

a. Hurrying causes mistakes, and then you save no time at all.

b. It is hard to forgive someone, but it is easy to make mistakes.

c. To get something, the only thing you need to do is look for it.

d. In certain situations, any action to reach an objective is justifiable.

e. Deal with a problem only when it arises.

f. Criminals are always punished for crimes.

g. Understand your limitations.

h. The winner gets the last laugh.

i. Not telling all of the truth is as misleading as telling a huge lie.

j. Hesitation might result in unpleasant outcomes.

Writing with Proverbs

Find the meaning of each proverb. (Use an online or print dictionary if necessary.) Then write a sentence for each proverb.

1. A chain is only as strong as its weakest link.

2. One of these days is none of these days.

3. He is not wise that is not wise for himself.

4. Never put off until tomorrow what can be done today.

5. The hand that rocks the cradle rules the world.

6. Those in glass houses should not throw stones.

7. All good things must come to an end.

8. He that hath a full purse never wanted a friend.

9. All things come to those who wait.

10. You can't make bricks without straw.

11. Don't hide your light under a bushel.

12. Fields have eyes, and woods have ears.

Denotation and Connotation

A word's dictionary definition is its **denotation**. This same word usually also has numerous **connotations**, or subjective meanings. These meanings the reader brings to the word. Words often have *positive*, *negative*, or *neutral* connotations.

To convey a precise idea, then, good writers employ subtle differences in denotation and connotation. For example, a character who is careful with money might be described as *frugal*, *thrifty*, *miserly*, *stingy*, or *abstemious*. Each word brings to mind a different image. Thoughtful writers select precise words deliberately and meticulously.

Consider these synonyms for the neutral word *refractory*:

willful *defiant* *unruly* *truculent*

Willful has a positive connotation, suggesting someone who has great determination to achieve an objective. *Defiant* is often used positively, but not always, and is sometimes used to describe someone who thinks for herself. *Unruly* and *truculent* have negative connotations. These words indicate disruption, aggression, and a willingness to fight.

Think: A willful legislator might struggle to draw attention to poverty, while an unruly witness might be disruptive in a court.

Look at these examples of words that are similar in denotation but have different connotations.

NEUTRAL	POSITIVE	NEGATIVE
ambivalent	**discerning**	**wishy-washy**
trainee	**protégé**	**flunkey**
lampoon	**satirize**	**ridicule**

Deciphering a word's denotation and its connotations is an important way to get the most out of what you read and to refine how you write.

Shades of Meaning

Write a plus sign (+) in the box if the word has a positive connotation. Write a minus sign (–) if the word has a negative connotation. Put a zero (0) if the word is neutral.

1. lackluster ☐ **2.** empathy ☐ **3.** ad hoc ☐ **4.** nepotism ☐

5. avatar ☐ **6.** beatitude ☐ **7.** incubus ☐ **8.** kudos ☐

9. lagniappe ☐ **10.** sycophant ☐ **11.** cataclysm ☐ **12.** debauch ☐

13. inchoate ☐ **14.** opt ☐ **15.** philistine ☐ **16.** savoir-faire ☐

Expressing the Connotation

Read each sentence. Select the word in parentheses that expresses the connotation (positive, negative, or neutral) given at the beginning of the sentence.

positive **1.** The main character is (**roguish, picaresque**) and survives by her wits alone.

neutral **2.** In the district tennis tournament, my longtime (**nemesis, adversary**) ended up beating me again.

negative **3.** Your behavior in front of those kind, elderly women makes me feel unquestionably (**queasy, unsettled**).

positive **4.** Our science teacher (**filled, imbued**) us with a great respect of the environment and the creatures in it.

negative **5.** The stand-up comic (**ridiculed, lampooned**) some young people in the audience until they exited.

negative **6.** Photographers (**bothered, beleaguered**) the movie star whenever she visited Los Angeles.

neutral **7.** Distant citizens quickly forgot about the (**damage, depredation**) that resulted from the hurricane.

neutral **8.** The young man was (**malleable, weak**) and so his parents worried he would not flourish in life.

Challenge: Using Connotation

Choose vocabulary words from Units 7–9 to replace the highlighted words in the sentences below. Then explain how the connotation of the replacement word changes the tone of the sentence.

fastidious	**aberration**	**mellifluous**
peccadillo	**pièce de résistance**	**malcontent**

1. The sculptor's **centerpiece** ____________________ at his first exhibition was a gargantuan and pliable replica of the Statue of Liberty.

____

____

2. Sylvia is especially worried about personal **iniquity** ____________________ and so strives to be self-aware and flawless.

____

____

3. Our mother's **neurotic** ____________________ attention to detail endured until she had grandchildren, and then she was finally more laid back.

____

____

Classical Roots

mal—bad, ill

This root appears in **malcontent** (page 101), which means "one who is dissatisfied with conditions." Some other words based on the same root are listed below.

maladapted	**malfeasance**	**malfunction**	**malingerer**
malaise	**malformation**	**malice**	**malodorous**

From the list of words above, choose the one that corresponds to each of the brief definitions below. Write the word in the blank space in the illustrative sentence below the definition. Use an online or print dictionary if necessary.

1. a desire to cause harm or suffering; deep-seated ill will
Legally, murder is distinguished from manslaughter by the element of _________________ aforethought.

2. having a bad odor; ill-smelling; highly improper
To my sensibilities, all blue-veined cheeses are unbearably _________________.

3. an abnormal or faulty bodily structure or part
The disease caused an unsightly _________________ of the patient's face.

4. one who pretends to be ill in order to escape duty or work
He was fired from the squad because he proved to be a shiftless _________________.

5. wrongdoing or misconduct in public office
The politician was accused of _________________ when the crooked scheme became public knowledge.

6. a vague feeling of physical or mental discomfort
For no evident reason, she was too beset by _________________ to attend class.

7. unsuited or poorly suited for a particular purpose or situation
The storage area was large enough, but it was _________________ for use as a classroom.

8. a failure to operate correctly or in a normal manner; to operate poorly or imperfectly
Radio contact was lost for over an hour because of a technical _________________.

UNIT 10

*Read the following selection, taking note of the **boldface** words and their contexts. These words are among those you will be studying in Unit 10. As you complete the exercises in this unit, it may help to refer to the way the words are used below.*

A River of English

<Humorous Essay>

Language is no **monolithic** edifice, hatched full-formed at the dawn of time, unchanging through the ages. A language is a living creature, sprung from the mouths and minds of the men and women who speak it. From one generation, from one neighborhood, from one speaker to the next, the river of language keeps flowing—and you can't step in the same river twice.

Things move fast in our modern world, and our language is one of those fast-moving entities, spurred by a rush of economic productivity and technological innovation. Each day, hoards of marketers assemble to coin new and improved brand names, catchy slogans, **fulsome** phrases fine-tuned to **dissimulate** the profit motive and manufacture demand. Scientists convene to agree on appropriate names for late-discovered organisms, particles, or **empirical** techniques. Each invention and discovery wants a catchy name. Each profession maintains a trendy lexicon of **apocryphal** jargon. Creative artists from Shakespeare to the latest song writer have increased the stock of our language in their quest for the **mot juste**.

The course of English is altered by wordsmiths in business, science, and art. But at its heart, linguistic change is driven by the accretion of unpredictable, near **imperceptible** transformations in the way we speak—and the way we speak is changing all the time.

Words enter our language, pass into common usage, and shift in meaning through the years. Four hundred years ago, highbrow English chefs borrowed from the French, using the word "**liaison**"

to characterize ingredients that hold a sauce together; today we're more likely to use the word to refer to people who facilitate cooperation among parts of an organization. Medieval alchemists steeped in Latin adopted the word "**sublimate**" to describe the act of heating liquid into vapor; centuries later, a psychologist with a metaphorical bent took the same word to name mental acts by which we refine our baser impulses into acceptable behavior. In the days of horse-powered transportation, the footman who ran errands for his master was called a **lackey**; we've retained the word to refer to slavish subordinates, or anyone who behaves like one and accepts unjust social **disparity**.

Among the most telling contributions to the language are simple, common phrases that color speech efficiently, without the obtrusiveness of more **flamboyant** locutions. In the nineteenth century, people who had to wait tried to "hold on," while those who aimed to hide sought to "hole up." Early twentieth-century English speakers who wanted a good look were the first to take a "gander," and those who heard a great deal were the first to have heard an "earful." Fresh colloquialisms often reflect the times they crop up in: As the gears of the industrial age churned ahead full steam, speakers thought to call a dull routine a "grind." By the mid-twentieth century, a project that was going well was "cooking with gas," while one faring poorly was going "down the tubes."

Bleary-eyed scholars peruse dusty tomes to determine the history of words and phrases in our language, as well as shifts in meaning over time. Occasionally they bring remarkable **acumen** to bear in **adjudicating** academic disputes about origins and rectifying **anachronisms** in the record. Fortunately, it takes less effort for most speakers to keep abreast of the twists and turns of the language. We just open our mouths, and the words come pouring out.

Snap the code, or go to
vocabularyworkshop.com

Note the spelling, pronunciation, part(s) of speech, and definition(s) of each of the following words. Then write the word in the blank spaces in the illustrative sentence(s) following. Finally, study the lists of synonyms and antonyms.

1. acumen (a kyü′ mən)

(*n.*) keenness of insight; quickness or accuracy of judgment

Stars who enjoy long careers generally choose their roles with remarkable ____________________.

SYNONYMS: perspicacity, shrewdness, acuity
ANTONYMS: ignorance, stupidity, obtuseness

2. adjudicate (ə jüd′ i kāt)

(*v.*) to act as judge in a matter; to settle through the use of a judge or legal tribunal

An arbitrator may sometimes ____________________ a civil suit involving a relatively small sum of money.

SYNONYMS: arbitrate, referee, mediate

3. anachronism (ə nak′ rə niz əm)

(*n.*) a chronological misplacing of events, objects, customs, or persons in regard to each other

To avoid introducing ____________________ into their work, authors of historical novels must do painstaking research.

SYNONYM: chronological error

4. apocryphal (ə pok′ rə fəl)

(*adj.*) of doubtful or questionable authenticity

Although his tales of youthful derring-do are probably ____________________, they are very entertaining.

SYNONYMS: fictitious, mythical, spurious, bogus
ANTONYMS: authentic, genuine, true

5. disparity (dis par′ ə tē)

(*n.*) a difference or inequality in age, rank, degree, amount, or quality; a dissimilarity, unlikeness

The growing ____________________ between the rich and the poor is a matter of grave concern.

SYNONYMS: discrepancy, incongruity
ANTONYMS: similarity, likeness, congruity

6. dissimulate (di sim′ yə lāt)

(*v.*) to hide or disguise one's true thoughts, feelings, or intentions

In awkward social situations, it is sometimes more courteous to ____________________ than to be straightforward.

SYNONYMS: pretend, misrepresent
ANTONYM: reveal

7. empirical
(em pir′ i kəl)

(*adj.*) derived from, dependent upon, or guided by practical experience, observation, or experiment, rather than by theory; so verifiable

The compilation of ____________________ data is an essential part of sound scientific research.

SYNONYMS: observed, pragmatic
ANTONYMS: theoretical, hypothetical, conjectural

8. flamboyant
(flam boi′ ənt)

(*adj.*) highly elaborate or ornate; vividly colored; strikingly brilliant or bold

We were dazzled by the ____________________ plumage of the birds in the tropical rain forest.

SYNONYMS: ostentatious, florid
ANTONYMS: staid, sedate, decorous, seemly, sober

9. fulsome
(fu̇l′ səm)

(*adj.*) offensively insincere or excessive; disgusting, sickening

It is best to take the ____________________ praise that appears in film previews with a grain of salt.

SYNONYMS: inordinate, repulsive
ANTONYMS: understated, muted, restrained, agreeable

10. immolate
(im′ ə lāt)

(*v.*) to kill as a sacrifice, especially by fire; to destroy or renounce for the sake of another

When the Aztecs took captives, they enslaved some and ____________________ others.

SYNONYM: kill; ANTONYMS: save, preserve

11. imperceptible
(im pər sep′ tə bəl)

(*adj.*) extremely slight; incapable of being perceived by the senses or the mind

When two candidates agree on most issues, voters may find the differences between them ____________________.

SYNONYMS: minimal, undetectable
ANTONYMS: conspicuous, noticeable, flagrant

12. lackey
(lak′ ē)

(*n.*) a uniformed male servant; a servile follower

A wealthy Victorian household generally included numerous maids, ____________________, and other domestics.

SYNONYMS: toady, flunky, hanger-on; ANTONYMS: lord, liege, boss

13. liaison
(lē′ ə zon)

(*n.*) the contact or means of communication between groups; someone acting as such a contact; any close relationship; a thickening or binding agent used in cooking

Block associations serve as ____________________ between neighborhoods and city governments.

SYNONYMS: intermediary, channel

14. monolithic
(mon ə lith′ ik)

(*adj.*) characterized by massiveness, solidness, and total uniformity

The government buildings in the state's capital can best be described as ________________ in style.

SYNONYMS: undifferentiated, massive, dense
ANTONYMS: diversified, variform, multifarious

15. mot juste
(mō zhüst′)

(*n.*) the most suitable or exact word or expression

The erudite film and theater critic always managed to find the ________________ to sum up her opinion.

ANTONYMS: misnomer, misusage, malapropism

16. nihilism
(nī′ əl iz əm)

(*n.*) a total rejection of existing laws; extreme radicalism

Those who rebel against the restraints imposed by society may be attracted to ________________.

ANTONYM: conservatism

17. patrician
(pə trish′ ən)

(*n.*) a member of the ruling class; a person of high rank; (*adj.*) belonging to, befitting, or characteristic of such a person

Though her origins were humble, she had the assurance and bearing of a ________________.

Many scions of ________________ families feel obliged to choose a life of public service.

SYNONYMS: (*n.*) aristocrat, peer; (*adj.*) highborn
ANTONYMS: (*n.*) commoner, plebeian

18. propitiate
(prō pish′ ē āt)

(*v.*) to make someone or something favorably inclined toward oneself; to conciliate, satisfy, or appease

Many ancient peoples practiced rituals involving offerings and sacrifices to ________________ their gods.

SYNONYM: mollify
ANTONYMS: alienate, provoke, annoy

19. sic
(sik)

(*adv.*) thus so; intentionally written so

When you see ________________ in a book, it is usually parenthetical, and it means that an obvious error was from an original text and thus to be left as is.

20. sublimate
(səb′ lə māt)

(*v.*) to redirect the energy of a biological or instinctive impulse into a higher or more acceptable channel

If we are to live in harmony with one another, we must learn to ________________ our aggressive impulses.

SYNONYM: elevate

Choosing the Right Word

*Select the **boldface** word that better completes each sentence. You might refer to the selection on pages 126–127 to see how most of these words are used in context.*

The London Eye Ferris wheel carries people to a height of 443 feet.

1. The London Eye, the famous Ferris wheel in Great Britain that opened to the general public in 2000, is both a (n) (**apocryphal, flamboyant**) display and a brilliant achievement.
2. Because deadly carbon monoxide gas can be neither seen nor smelled, its presence is practically (**empirical, imperceptible**).
3. There is probably nothing worse than having (**patrician, apocryphal**) tastes on an income better suited to the lifestyle of a pauper.
4. I agree that there are imperfections in our society, but I cannot accept your (**imperceptible, nihilistic**) belief that the entire past must be discarded.
5. The main character is a bumbling inventor who has accidentally transported himself back to the past, there to suffer the misadventures of a hapless (**lackey, anachronism**).
6. There seemed no point in the author's gratuitous use of such (**fulsome, apocryphal**) language other than to offend the taste of the reader.
7. The story about Bunker Hill with its warning, "Don't fire until you see the whites of their eyes," may be (**monolithic, apocryphal**), but I'm going to continue believing it.
8. The cost of (**adjudication, dissimulation**) often exceeds the amount of the award.
9. In a pluralistic democracy, such as the United States, there is little chance that a (**flamboyant, monolithic**) public opinion will ever develop on any controversial issue.
10. Though Plato's approach to philosophy often seems somewhat mystical, Aristotle's is decidedly (**empirical, fulsome**).
11. No country can survive the threats of foreign invasion and domestic insurrection unless it is governed by leaders with extraordinary political (**acumen, disparity**).
12. We are not suggesting that students should run the school, but we believe that the administration should maintain a (**nihilism, liaison**) with the students.
13. In a campaign speech, the candidate said, "My opponent has flaunted (**[sic], mot juste**) all of the principles of sound fiscal management."
14. When you say that your rival has a talent for (**disparity, dissimulation**), what you really mean is that he is an out-and-out phony.
15. American voters may be amused by a (**patrician, flamboyant**) personality, but they seem to prefer more sober types when making their choice for high public office.

16. Some psychologists theorize that genius in any field represents a special kind of (**immolation, sublimation**) of capacities, drives, and needs that are in all of us.

17. Those solemn religious ceremonies are intended to protect the tribe from disasters by (**propitiating, adjudicating**) the gods who control natural phenomena.

18. It's no wonder he's got such a swelled head when all those (**patricians, lackeys**) tagging along after him do nothing but sing his praises.

19. There is often a (**liaison, disparity**) between what people aspire to do and what they are equipped to do by natural endowment and training.

20. People who engage in self-destructive behavior seem to have a desire to (**propitiate, immolate**) themselves.

21. Most students failed the midterm exam, but they were able to (**adjudicate, propitiate**) their teacher by forming study groups for second semester.

22. As she is descended from a long line of (**liaisons, patricians**), at a fine restaurant she expects haute cuisine, attentive and meticulous waitstaff, and a resident wine steward.

23. She is so concerned with words that she seems to think the only thing that is needed to deal with a problem is to find the (**mot juste, anachronism**) to describe it.

24. If you choose to call me your (**lackey, malleable**), and not your butler, I will be forced to look elsewhere for work.

25. A breeder of dogs, my uncle was asked to (**adjudicate, immolate**) at the local dog show.

Synonyms

*Choose the word from this unit that is the same or most nearly the same in meaning as the **boldface** word or expression in the phrase. Write that word on the line. Use a dictionary if necessary.*

1. to **slay** those enemies in their path ____________
2. based on **experiential** evidence ____________
3. learned to **rechannel** their impulses ____________
4. known for wearing **garish** outfits ____________
5. has a tendency to **dissemble** ____________
6. sought to **placate** their supervisor ____________
7. a paralyzing and **extreme skepticism** ____________
8. an austere and refined **noble** from the castle ____________
9. said it was a pitty [**thus so**] ____________
10. sought the **right word** with which to end the speech ____________

Antonyms

*Choose the word from this unit that is most nearly opposite in meaning to the **boldface** word or expression in the phrase. Write that word on the line. Use a dictionary if necessary.*

1. descended from **peasants** ____________________
2. **estrange** his family by disparaging them ____________________
3. a group that espouses **political caution** ____________________
4. a plan to **rescue** the hostages ____________________
5. willingly worked hard for his **employer** ____________________

Completing the Sentence

From the words in this unit, choose the one that best completes each of the following sentences. Write the word in the space provided.

1. It is one thing to spin out ingenious theories; it is quite another to find ____________________ confirmation for them.

2. I know you're trying to curry favor with the boss, but must you greet every one of his bright ideas with such ____________________ flattery?

3. In calling them "stinkers," I may not have been too refined; but in view of their disgraceful conduct, I think I applied the ____________________.

4. The aggressive drive can be channeled into antisocial forms of behavior or ____________________ into loftier, more worthwhile endeavors.

5. A major political party in the United States represents a coalition of many different views and interests, rather than a(n) ____________________ structure.

6. His efforts to ____________________ his feelings of inadequacy by pretending to be bored and indifferent are a sign of immaturity.

7. Having the Civil War general sign documents with a ballpoint pen struck me as the most ludicrous ____________________ in the whole miniseries.

8. During the early years of the Roman Republic, plebeians vied bitterly with ____________________ for political dominance.

9. Their blanket rejection of the standards and values on which our society is founded seems to be little short of senseless ____________________.

10. One would expect such ____________________ behavior from an attention-seeking celebrity, not from a normally shy, unassuming person.

11. The company's profits increased remarkably last year, thanks mainly to the new president's exceptional business ____________________.

12. Although these stories have been widely accepted for many years, we now have ample evidence to show that they are completely ____________________.

13. Then she leaned toward me and said confidingly, "Between you and I ____________________, I didn't believe a word he said."

14. As the duke's coach drew up, two ____________________ in splendid livery stepped forth to open the carriage door.

15. The fate of individuals accused of war crimes may be ____________________ by an international court.

16. The able auctioneer acknowledged bids from the audience that were so discreet as to be ____________________ to the untrained eye.

17. What a shock it was for her to discover the unworthiness of the cause for which she had ____________________ her youth, her talents, and her hopes of happiness.

18. We need not try actively to ____________________ the opponents of our candidate, but we can certainly take reasonable precautions to avoid antagonizing them.

19. During the campaign in West Virginia in 1861, Robert E. Lee acted as the ____________________ between the commanders of the two independent Confederate brigades operating in the area.

20. Though I believed their promises at first, I soon came to realize the great ____________________ between their words and their deeds.

Writing: Words in Action

1. Look back at "A River of English" (pages 126–127). Think about the slang and phrases that young people commonly use today. Also consider words and phrases you've heard that were common among previous generations. Write a compare-contrast essay examining youth language and slang then and now. Use at least two details from the passage and three unit words.

2. In "A River of English" (refer to pages 126–127), the writer notes, "from one speaker to the next, the river of language keeps flowing." In the United States, some federal and state legislators have proposed bills to require use of the English language and to end bilingual education, for example. Write at least three paragraphs in the style of an email to a legislator, using three or more words from this unit, in which you convince your representative to either vote for, or against, English-only legislation.

Vocabulary in Context

Literary Text

*The following excerpts are from works by H.L. Mencken. Some of the words you have studied in this unit appear in **boldface** type. Complete each statement below the excerpt by circling the letter of the correct answer.*

1. Of the intrinsic differences that separate American from English the chief have their roots in the obvious **disparity** between the environment and traditions of the American people since the seventeenth century and those of the English. (*The American Language*)

If there is a **disparity**, there is a

a. misunderstanding **c.** disguise
b. clarity **d.** gap

2. *Philadelphia*, got its name from the ancient stronghold of Philadelphus of Pergamun. To make up for the falling off of this old and **flamboyant** custom, the more recent immigrants have brought with them the names of the capitals and other great cities of their fatherlands. (*The American Language*)

Something that is **flamboyant** is also

a. minimal **c.** ridiculous
b. conspicuous **d.** solemn

H.L. Mencken, American critic, journalist, editor, and publisher, lived in Baltimore for much of his life.

3. The best and most intellectual ... are not men, but women, and so are the best teachers and blackmailers ... In the demimonde one will find enough **acumen** and daring, and enough resilience in the face of special difficulties, to put the equipment of any exclusively male profession to shame. (*In Defense of Women*)

Acumen is also

a. shrewdness **c.** talent
b. splendor **d.** potential

4. On the one hand, he is a prodigy of learning, a veritable warehouse of musical information, true, half-true and **apocryphal**; on the other hand, he is a jester who delights in reducing all learning to absurdity. (*A Book of Prefaces*)

Something that is **apocryphal** is

a. authoritative **c.** catastrophic
b. outrageous **d.** dubious

5. They began by howling their sins from the mourners' bench; they came to their end, many of them, in the supreme **immolation** of battle. (*A Book of Prefaces*)

An **immolation** is NOT a(n)

a. sacrifice **c.** ruination
b. redemption **d.** eradication

Snap the code, or go to **vocabularyworkshop.com**

*Read the following selection, taking note of the **boldface** words and their contexts. These words are among those you will be studying in Unit 11. As you complete the exercises in this unit, it may help to refer to the way the words are used below.*

Remarks Prepared for Delivery Before Congress

<Script for Political Speech>

Esteemed colleagues and fellow citizens, good morning:

Our nation faces a stark choice between entering, ill-advisedly, into a war against an amorphous enemy, or remaining at peace. Before we rush to send citizens into harm's way, before we commit resources for years to come, we must let the lessons of history guide us.

Twenty-eight centuries ago, after years of fighting, the Athenian and Trojan armies were at an **impasse** until the Greeks employed a bold and **parlous** tactic. Unable to penetrate King Priam's Troy by force, the Greek army breeched the walls with **bravado** and cunning. They built a colossal hollow wooden horse, left it outside the fortress, and feigned departure. Many Trojan leaders suspected treachery and reasoned that receiving an offering from their ruthless enemy was a **non sequitur**. Nonetheless, in a calamitous example of **quixotic** thinking, Priam had the horse pulled inside. This gift **metamorphosed** into a treacherous trick. Athenian warriors emerged from within the hollow horse that night and opened the gates of Troy for their army, which was poised to continue the **vendetta**. Troy was ransacked.

This legendary episode exemplifies a trait of governments that historians deem "folly." Despite leaders' capacity for wisdom, even brilliance, a puzzling **dichotomy** exists: Governments chronically act in a manner contrary to their own interests, despite the availability of viable alternatives.

Take Montezuma, who made a fateful decision that cost him dearly. Five centuries ago, he ruled a wealthy, sophisticated Mesoamerican empire of five million people. Despite warnings from advisors, he fell prey to Cortez and his 600 soldiers, 17 horses, and 10 cannon. While a huge Aztec army stood by, Montezuma,

President Obama looks at a speech, 2009.

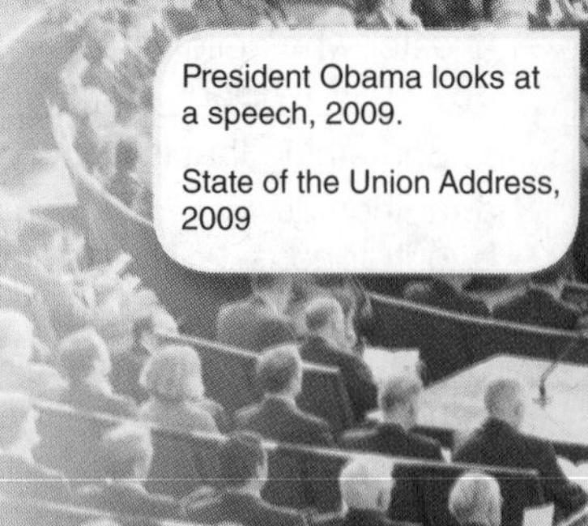

State of the Union Address, 2009

fooled by the Spaniard's **mystique** into thinking him a returning god, gave the conquistador safe passage into the city, and soon after found himself captured.

Consider the ill-advised choice the British government made in dealing with its disconsolate American colony, where there was no clear **consensus** for revolt. Options in England abounded for compromises that could have **constricted** the increase in grievances and mended fences, but instead, its government opted to use force. Suppressing an independence movement in a colony more than 1000 miles long and 3000 miles away proved to be an expensive miscalculation for the British.

And lastly, remember Pearl Harbor. The Japanese should have learned from a fateful blunder the German Kaiser made in World War I when, by attacking American shipping, the Kaiser made a reluctant nation his enemy. The United States sent two million soldiers to Europe, thus ending Germany's attempt to dominate that continent. Japan, in its zeal to establish an Asian Pacific empire, repeated the Kaiser's folly when, despite having reasonable alternatives, its government opted for bombing the U.S. Pacific fleet. It was a terrible miscalculation. Instead of gaining the empire it sought, Japan enjoyed a moment of **euphoria**, but then suffered catastrophic defeat.

When individuals exhibit a lack of normal prudence or foresight, it's regrettable, but when governments do, it's tragic. Whatever causes folly—impulse, ambition, prejudice, hubris—is antithetical to the **sine qua non** of government: to rule reasonably in the interest of its people. And that's what we *must* do right here in this chamber. Look no further than our recent **quagmires** abroad to see the disheartening results of past folly—we dare not repeat such mistakes this day. Say "No" to the **effusive** beating of the drums of war and let us not follow the dangerous path that has tempted so many of our predecessors. Thank you.

iWords™

Snap the code, or go to **vocabularyworkshop.com**

Note the spelling, pronunciation, part(s) of speech, and definition(s) of each of the following words. Then write the word in the blank spaces in the illustrative sentence(s) following. Finally, study the lists of synonyms and antonyms.

1. apostate (ə pos′ tāt)

(*n.*) one who forsakes his or her religion, party, or cause

A politician who switches parties can expect to be denounced by former allies as an ____________.

SYNONYMS: renegade, defector
ANTONYM: true believer

2. bravado (brə vä′ dō)

(*n.*) a display of false or assumed courage

The challenger's boast that he would knock the champ out in the first round was sheer ____________.

SYNONYMS: swagger, bluster, braggadocio
ANTONYMS: mettle, bravery, pluck

3. consensus (kən sen′ səs)

(*n.*) a collective or general agreement of opinion, feeling, or thinking

After an unusually contentious debate, the council finally reached a ____________.

SYNONYMS: unanimity, concord, accord, harmony
ANTONYMS: dissension, discord, disagreement

4. constrict (kən strikt′)

(*v.*) to make smaller or narrower, draw together, squeeze; to stop or cause to falter

An accident or road repairs might ____________ the flow of traffic on a busy highway.

SYNONYMS: contract, curb, restrain
ANTONYMS: enlarge, dilate, expand

5. dichotomy (dī kot′ ə mē)

(*n.*) a division into two contradictory or mutually exclusive parts; a branching or forking in an ancestral line

Many of the world's great works of literature examine the ____________ between good and evil.

SYNONYMS: schism, bifurcation
ANTONYMS: uniformity, oneness

6. effusive (i fyü′ siv)

(*adj.*) highly demonstrative; unrestrained

I received such an ____________ welcome from my hosts that I felt like the party's guest of honor.

SYNONYMS: gushy, lavish
ANTONYMS: restrained, reserved, muted, subdued

7. euphoria (yü fōr′ ē ə)

(*n.*) a feeling of great happiness or well-being, often with no objective basis

It is perfectly normal for a person who wins the lottery to feel an initial surge of ____________________.

SYNONYMS: elation, bliss, ecstasy, rapture
ANTONYMS: melancholy, depression, gloom

8. gothic (goth′ ik)

(*adj.*) characterized by or emphasizing a gloomy setting and grotesque or violent events; such a literary or artistic style; a type of medieval architecture

In many a ____________________ novel, the life of the brooding protagonist is blighted by a dark secret.

SYNONYM: sinister

9. impasse (im′ pas)

(*n.*) a dead end; a position from which there is no escape; a problem to which there is no solution

When negotiations reached an ____________________, the workers went out on strike.

SYNONYMS: standoff, stalemate

10. lugubrious (lu̇ gü′ brē əs)

(*adj.*) sad, mournful, or gloomy, especially to an exaggerated or ludicrous degree

The clown's ____________________ face, complete with a painted teardrop, never fails to make the audience laugh.

SYNONYMS: doleful, melancholy, dismal
ANTONYMS: jovial, hilarious, funny

11. metamorphosis (met ə môr′ fə sis)

(*n.*) a complete transformation, as if by magic

The beauty makeovers that we sometimes see on television are a kind of ____________________.

SYNONYMS: change, makeover

12. mystique (mi stēk′)

(*n.*) an aura or attitude of mystery or veneration surrounding something or someone

A ____________________ still clings to some of the great movie stars of the past.

SYNONYM: charisma

13. non sequitur (non sek′ wi tər)

(*n.*) an inference or conclusion that does not follow logically from the facts or premises

When it was the next debater's turn, he confounded us with an argument undermined by ____________________.

SYNONYMS: illogical reference, unsound conclusion

14. parlous (pär′ ləs)

(*adj.*) full of danger or risk, perilous

In a televised speech, the president warned the nation that it would face ____________ times.

SYNONYMS: hazardous, risky, dangerous
ANTONYMS: safe, secure, risk-free

15. punctilio (pəŋk til′ ē ō)

(*n.*) a minute detail of conduct or procedure; an instant of time

The mark of a true perfectionist is the need to check each and every ____________ personally.

SYNONYM: nicety

16. quagmire (kwag′ mīr)

(*n.*) soft, soggy mud or slush; a difficult or entrapping situation

After a week of heavy rain, the farmer's fields were reduced to a ____________.

SYNONYMS: fen, marsh, morass
ANTONYMS: bedrock, solid footing, terra firma

17. quixotic (kwik sot′ ik)

(*adj.*) extravagantly or romantically idealistic; visionary without regard to practical considerations

Utopian fiction presents ____________ fantasies of ideal social orders.

SYNONYMS: fanciful, impractical, utopian
ANTONYMS: realistic, down-to-earth, pragmatic

18. raconteur (rak on tər′)

(*n.*) a person who tells stories and anecdotes with great skill

The author, a noted ____________, was much sought after as a dinner party guest.

SYNONYM: anecdotist

19. sine qua non (sin ə kwä nōn′)

(*n.*) an essential or indispensable element or condition

The ____________ for a successful party is a group of interesting and sociable guests.

SYNONYMS: necessity, desideratum

20. vendetta (ven det′ ə)

(*n.*) a prolonged feud, often between two families, characterized by retaliatory acts of revenge; any act motivated by vengeance

The two novelists, once good friends, have been carrying on a literary ____________ for more than two decades.

SYNONYMS: blood feud, rivalry

Choosing the Right Word

*Select the **boldface** word that better completes each sentence. You might refer to the selection on pages 136–137 to see how most of these words are used in context.*

Olivia Hussey and Leonard Whiting star in the 1968 film version of *Romeo and Juliet*.

1. In *Romeo and Juliet*, the hero's tragic death comes as the result of a long-standing (**vendetta, bravado**) between his family and Juliet's.
2. Involvement in the long war in Vietnam led the United States into a (**consensus, quagmire**) from which it was extremely difficult to withdraw.
3. Though your efforts to enact a program of ecological reform in the face of strong opposition were (**quixotic, gothic**) and doomed to failure, they were inspiring.
4. It's laughable of you to think that you are an accomplished (**raconteur, apostate**) just because you have memorized an assortment of feeble old jokes.
5. The new assistant dean's adherence to every (**mystique, punctilio**) in the Student Code alienated both the faculty and the student body.
6. Very few of the world's problems can be understood in terms of a simple (**euphoria, dichotomy**) of right and wrong.
7. Despite the grave risks that the rescue attempt would entail, there was no shortage of volunteers for the (**parlous, effusive**) undertaking.
8. Does it seem paradoxical that, like many other great comedians, she goes about with a characteristically (**lugubrious, quixotic**) expression on her face?
9. The ordeal of the Civil War (**apostatized, metamorphosed**) Lincoln from an obscure small-town lawyer into an historical personality of universal appeal.
10. Mr. Ridley is fascinated by the Middle Ages and (**mellifluous, gothic**) architecture; therefore, he plans to travel around Europe this summer.
11. Diana spent a year abroad her junior year, and, when she returned, I immediately recognized a complete, and pleasantly surprising, (**metamorphosis, dichotomy**).
12. As we learned to understand each other's needs and aspirations, a sort of unspoken (**consensus, impasse**) developed that enabled us to work together harmoniously.
13. Perhaps her volunteering to undertake the mission was mere (**bravado, consensus**), but the fact remains that she accomplished a great deal.
14. Space suits are designed to afford astronauts maximum protection without unduly (**constricting, dichotomizing**) their freedom of movement.
15. There are times when I like to read a (**gothic, parlous**) tale of gloomy castles, mysterious strangers, and unhappy romances.

16. Their analysis of the problem seemed to me extremely fallacious—full of false assumptions, dubious generalizations, and (**constrictions, non sequiturs**).

17. Even though their son had abandoned the religion in which he had been brought up, his parents never thought of him as an (**apostate, impasse**).

18. For a long time we lived under the illusion that "everything would come out all right," but, inevitably, we arrived at the (**vendetta, impasse**) where we had to face realities.

19. Our thesis was that, at this stage in their history, Americans must eschew the (**sine qua non**, **mystique**) of force and violence and develop new ideals of social cooperation.

20. I wanted a direct, factual explanation of what had happened, but all I got were emotional (**effusions, quagmires**) describing in painful detail how much they had suffered.

21. After the downpour the first night, our camping trip became nightmarish, as we had to drag our supplies through fallen limbs and trudge through a (**punctilio, quagmire**).

22. Aaron Burr, the third United States Vice President, concluded a (**bane, vendetta**) against Alexander Hamilton, the first United States Secretary of the Treasury, by killing him in a duel in 1804.

23. It is impossible for me to convey the intensity of emotion that I felt at that (**lugubrious, euphoric**) moment when I learned that I had won the scholarship.

24. There is no point in trying to decide exactly which of the factors is most important for victory in the election; every one of them is a (**non sequitur, sine qua non**).

25. Your prose is (**effusive, parlous**), heartfelt, and unrivaled—an absolute pleasure to read.

Synonyms

Choose the word from this unit that is the same or most nearly the same in meaning as the ***boldface*** *word or expression in the phrase. Write that word on the line. Use a dictionary if necessary.*

1. attend to each **fine point** myself ____________

2. a **turncoat** reviled by all ____________

3. unable to break the **deadlock** ____________

4. the glaring **division** between wealth and poverty ____________

5. an **eerie** story of betrayal and madness ____________

6. **dolorous** lamentations of the poodle ____________

7. a **storyteller** without equal ____________

8. stuck in the **bog** ____________

9. a **requisite** for good health ____________

10. underwent a truly remarkable **transformation** ____________

Antonyms

*Choose the word from this unit that is most nearly opposite in meaning to the **boldface** word or expression in the phrase. Write that word on the line. Use a dictionary if necessary.*

1. only concerned with the **big ideas** ____________
2. a **man of few words** with few friends and relations ____________
3. sang a **merry** ballad ____________
4. a **wholesome** and sunny romance novel ____________
5. has a reputation for being a **loyalist** ____________

Completing the Sentence

From the words in this unit, choose the one that best completes each of the following sentences. Write the word in the space provided.

1. Not until later did I realize that their ____________ expressions of interest in our welfare were insincere and self-serving.

2. Ernest Hemingway's *Death in the Afternoon* offers a rare insight into the ____________ of the bullring and the attitudes that surround that ancient blood sport.

3. To achieve an hourglass figure, fashionable ladies of the nineteenth century employed tight-fitting corsets to ____________ their waistlines.

4. Modern military power requires great industrial resources, but to conclude from this that industrialized nations are inherently militaristic is a ____________.

5. The police investigation established that the victim was not an innocent bystander but the target of a gangland ____________.

6. The speakers said that they could see little hope for world peace unless something could be done to bridge the ____________ between the "have" and the "have-not" nations.

7. His challenge to fight was pure ____________; inwardly he hoped that no one would take him on.

8. Although it may be true that hard work does not guarantee success, it is certainly a(n) ____________ for doing well in any endeavor.

9. Every great President must combine various roles: the practical politician, the masterful intellectual, the tough administrator, the persuasive advocate—and at least a touch of the ____________ visionary.

10. One look at the coach's ____________ expression, and I knew that all our misgivings about the outcome of the game had been borne out.

11. The rugged landscape, with the severe vertical lines of the mountains in the background, lent an air of ____________________ gloom to the entire scene.

12. Though everyone in our club agreed that we had a problem, there was no group ____________________ on how to solve it.

13. As the disappointing results of the poll filtered in, the candidate sank into a(n) ____________________ of doubts about the future.

14. The mood of ____________________ brought about by our extraordinary good fortune caused us to relax our usual alertness.

15. Each episode in the silent-movie serial *The Perils of Pauline* ended with the heroine facing another ____________________ predicament.

16. You cannot duck your responsibility for negotiating an agreement simply by announcing that you have reached a hopeless ____________________.

17. When he came to the throne, the ____________________ renounced the established religion and began a vigorous campaign to reestablish paganism as the official belief system of the region.

18. The man was a skilled ____________________ whose repertory of amusing anecdotes was seemingly inexhaustible.

19. It took Rome centuries to achieve the miraculous ____________________ from a minor city-state along the Tiber to the leading power in the Mediterranean world.

20. How can you concern yourself with the ____________________ of protocol when your whole world is collapsing about your ears?

Writing: Words in Action

1. Look back at "Remarks Prepared for Delivery Before Congress" (pages 136–137). Suppose you are a legislator who was swayed by this political speech. Write a statement to your constituents, using at least three details from the passage and three unit words, in which you explain and defend why you voted against "folly."

2. *"As long as war is regarded as wicked, it will always have its fascinations. When it is looked upon as vulgar, it will cease to be popular."—Oscar Wilde*

   Do you agree with Wilde? Support your opinion with specific examples from your studies, reading (refer to pages 136–137), or personal observations and experience. Write at least three paragraphs, and use three or more unit words.

Vocabulary in Context

Literary Text

*The following excerpts are from works by Mark Twain. Some of the words you have studied in this unit appear in **boldface** type. Complete each statement below the excerpt by circling the letter of the correct answer.*

1. He sprung his secret about Huck's share in the adventure in the finest dramatic manner he was master of, but the surprise it occasioned was largely counterfeit and not as clamorous and **effusive** as it might have been under happier circumstances. (*The Adventures of Tom Sawyer*)

To be **effusive** is to be

a. enthusiastic **c.** remote
b. riotous **d.** taciturn

2. They continued to whisper for some little time. Presently a dog set up a long, **lugubrious** howl just outside—within ten feet of them. The boys clasped each other suddenly, in an agony of fright. (*The Adventures of Tom Sawyer*)

Something that is **lugubrious** is

a. petrifying **c.** outrageous
b. woeful **d.** mawkish

"Huck and Tom ran for their lives" in *The Adventures of Tom Sawyer*.

3. In the principal street of the city, it had received more attention; for hogs; great and small, rooted about in it and wallowed in it, turning the street into a liquid **quagmire** which could only be crossed on pieces of plank thrown here and there. (*The Gilded Age*)

A **quagmire** is like a(n)

a. dissection **c.** crag
b. enclosure **d.** swamp

4. "By the right of friendship," interrupted Philip stoutly. "It may matter little to you. It is everything to him. He has a **quixotic** notion that you would turn back from what is before you for his sake. You cannot be ignorant of what all the city is talking of." (*The Gilded Age*)

A **quixotic** notion is NOT

a. absurd **c.** commonsensical
b. eccentric **d.** whimsical

5. I had some talk with him about the war times; but ... the discourse fell upon "feuds," for in no part of the South has the **vendetta** flourished more briskly, or held out longer between warring families, than in this particular region. (*Life on the Mississippi*)

A **vendetta** is a

a. prosperity **c.** serenity
b. rivalry **d.** fable

Snap the code, or go to **vocabularyworkshop.com**

*Read the following selection, taking note of the **boldface** words and their contexts. These words are among those you will be studying in Unit 12. As you complete the exercises in this unit, it may help to refer to the way the words are used below.*

Matriarchal Society

<Expository Essay>

Throughout recorded history, almost all cultures and countries have been patriarchal—controlled by men—with women relegated to second-class status. Have there been **viable** matriarchal societies in which women played important, **apposite** roles in every area of family, social, and political life? Most historians and anthropologists say no, although there have been scattered instances of quasi-matriarchal, or matrilineal, cultures in Africa, in Asia, among a few Native American tribes, and for a short time, in Hawaii. (In a matrilineal society, ancestral descent is traced through the maternal line.)

Nubian queen Amanirenas

Some ancient African societies did experience periods of matriarchy, and goddess worship was common. For example, the ancient Nubians, a northern African culture of great influence and power, worshipped Isis, the all-knowing mother figure and, for a time, women dominated Nubian life. Historical evidence suggests that Nubia had an exceptionally large number of ruling queens and princesses (at least 10 have been identified). **Charismatic** warrior-queen Amanirenas is one; she led her armies into **precarious** battle against soldiers of the **narcissistic** Roman Emperor Augustus Caesar, whose **execrable**, land-grabbing behavior did not **augur** well for the Nubians.

A theory has been posited that numerous goddess-worshipping cultures in antiquity existed—and that women ruled many places on Earth before men seized power. This theory is controversial and **impinges** on commonly held popular beliefs. While some anthropologists are convinced of its legitimacy and are exploring **labyrinthian** ancient writings and artifacts for new clues, others view the idea of women ruling the world as a false utopia, or even a **zany** myth or fantasy pushed forward by feminist **zealots**.

While examples of true matriarchies may be rare, gender-egalitarian societies and ideologies—with men and women enjoying a natural **rapport** and living on more or less equal footing—have existed and continue to exist in some parts of the world. And women have significant power, prestige, and autonomy even in cultures where men are the formal leaders. These societies have some commonalities: a strong respect for women as mothers, a closeness with nature and the natural

An Onondaga woman of the Iroquois nation

A Minangkabau woman with a traditional headdress

world, an emphasis on the **utilitarian**, and a **pastiche** of gender roles. The Iroquois nations of North America have matrilineal customs, and family houses were owned by the oldest women members.

Today, in West Sumatra, Indonesia, some Minangkabau people practice a form of matriarchy, but it is not a mirror-opposite of patriarchy and it is subject to the **vagaries** of modern life. The Minangkabau follow matrilineal customs and a nature-based philosophy called "adat," which places an emphasis on nurturing growth and the maternal. Traditionally, women elders are revered and respected and women control land inheritance. But neither sex "rules"—decision-making is by consensus, with an ongoing partnership in place between the sexes for the common good.

Snap the code, or go to **vocabularyworkshop.com**

Definitions

Note the spelling, pronunciation, part(s) of speech, and definition(s) of each of the following words. Then write the word in the blank spaces in the illustrative sentence(s) following. Finally, study the lists of synonyms and antonyms.

1. apposite (ap′ ə zit)

(*adj.*) appropriate; suitable; apt

I did my best to give an ____________ answer to each of the interviewer's questions.

SYNONYMS: pertinent, material, germane
ANTONYMS: irrelevant, immaterial, inappropriate

2. augur (ô′ ger)

(*n.*) a prophet or seer; (*v.*) to predict, foreshadow

The old man who lived alone in the forest was believed by the villagers to be an ____________.

The news did not ____________ well for the health of the economy in the short term.

SYNONYMS: (*n.*) oracle; (*v.*) bode

3. bilk (bilk)

(*v.*) to defraud, cheat, or swindle; to evade payment of; to frustrate, thwart

There will always be people who are only too ready to ____________ credulous individuals.

SYNONYM: cozen

4. charisma (kə riz′ mə)

(*n.*) the special personal magnetism that makes an individual exceptionally appealing to other people; a divinely bestowed gift or power

According to leading pundits, the dynamic young politician has the ____________ of a born leader.

SYNONYMS: appeal, charm, mystique

5. debilitate (di bil′ ə tāt)

(*v.*) to make weak or feeble

Illness ____________ the patient so severely that she was no longer able to perform even the simplest everyday chores.

SYNONYMS: enervate, sap, exhaust
ANTONYMS: strengthen, invigorate

6. execrable (ek′ si krə bəl)

(*adj.*) utterly detestable, hateful, or abhorrent; extremely inferior

The crude and ____________ behavior of a few individuals spoiled the evening for the rest of us.

SYNONYMS: odious, abominable, reprehensible
ANTONYMS: commendable, praiseworthy, meritorious

7. impinge (im pinj′)

(*v.*) to strike against or collide with violently; to encroach or obtrude upon; to make an impression upon

Political forces sometimes ____________ on our everyday lives.

SYNONYMS: horn in, affect

8. labyrinth (lab′ ə rinth)

(*n.*) a bewildering maze; any confusing or complicated situation

I quickly lost my way as I wandered through the old city's ____________ of winding streets.

SYNONYMS: tangle, mystery, enigma

9. narcissism (när′ sə siz əm)

(*n.*) excessive self-love; absorption in oneself

Because of her ____________, she was completely unwilling to listen to other people's opinions.

SYNONYMS: egotism, conceit, vanity, amour propre

10. pastiche (pas tēsh′)

(*n.*) a dramatic, musical, or literary work made up of bits and pieces from other sources; a hodgepodge

The figure skater performed to a ____________ of melodies from Richard Wagner's operas.

SYNONYMS: medley, melange, potpourri

11. penultimate (pe nəl′ tə mit)

(*adj.*) next to the last

In the relay race, our team was losing until the ____________ lap when our best runner swiftly moved to first place.

SYNONYM: intermediate; ANTONYM: terminal

12. precarious (pri kâr′ ē əs)

(*adj.*) very uncertain or unsure; dangerous or risky

A long period of unemployment left my friend in a financially ____________ position.

SYNONYMS: perilous, dubious, ticklish; ANTONYMS: safe, sturdy, firm

13. rapport (ra pôr′)

(*n.*) a close and harmonious relationship

The players in a chamber music ensemble need to develop an excellent ____________.

SYNONYMS: tie, affinity, understanding

14. utilitarian (yü til ə târ′ ē ən)

(*adj.*) stressing practicality over other considerations; relating to the belief that what is good or desirable is determined purely by its usefulness

The layout and organization of the busy restaurant's small kitchen were strictly ____________.

SYNONYMS: practical, functional, pragmatic
ANTONYMS: nonfunctional, ornamental, decorative

15. vacuous (vak′ yü əs)

(*adj.*) devoid of matter, substance, or meaning; lacking ideas or intelligence; purposeless

From the ____________ expression on your face, no one would guess that you have such a sharp mind.

SYNONYMS: inane, fatuous, void, empty
ANTONYMS: incisive, perceptive, intelligent

16. vagary (vā′ gə rē)

(*n.*) an unpredictable, erratic, or seemingly purposeless action, occurrence, or notion

Who can explain the ____________ of the world of high fashion?

SYNONYMS: caprice, quirk

17. viable (vī′ ə bəl)

(*adj.*) capable of living or developing under normal circumstances

The mayor announced a ____________ plan to reduce traffic in the downtown business district.

SYNONYMS: practicable, workable, feasible
ANTONYMS: impracticable, unworkable, unfeasible

18. xenophobia (zen ə fō′ bē ə)

(*n.*) undue or unreasonable fear, hatred, or contempt of foreigners or strangers or of what is foreign or strange

It is sad when people who themselves were once newcomers to a land are blinded by ____________.

SYNONYMS: provinciality, parochialism

19. zany (zā′ nē)

(*adj.*) clownish or funny in a crazy, bizarre, or ludicrous way; (*n.*) one who plays the clown

Who doesn't love the ____________ antics of the Marx brothers?

In every sitcom, there is a goofy character who can best be described as a ____________.

SYNONYMS: (*adj.*) comical, daffy; (*n.*) buffoon
ANTONYMS: (*adj.*) sedate, decorous, prim, sober, grave

20. zealot (zel′ ət)

(*n.*) a fanatical partisan; an ardent follower

When it comes to our school's hockey team, my brother can best be described as a ____________.

SYNONYMS: fanatic, extremist

Choosing the Right Word

*Select the **boldface** word that better completes each sentence. You might refer to the selection on pages 146–147 to see how most of these words are used in context.*

1. It was the function of a Roman (**augur, zany**) to divine the will of the gods through the interpretation of various natural phenomena, including the flight of birds.

2. Succeeding in business is comparable not to advancing along a straight line but rather to finding one's way through an uncharted, (**labyrinthine, apposite**) passage.

3. How can you be so easily impressed by those (**vacuous, precarious**) generalizations and clichés?

4. The disease had such a(n) (**debilitating, execrable**) effect upon her constitution that she was unable to return to work for almost a year.

5. Their optimism is so unwavering and so all-encompassing that bad news simply fails to (**impinge, bilk**) on their confidence.

The ancient Roman sky god, Jupiter, was often honored on the tops of hills or mountains.

6. In condemning their (**apposite, execrable**) conduct, let us not assume that we ourselves are completely free of blame.

7. I have no sympathy for those who have allowed themselves to be (**impinged, bilked**) by such an obvious get-rich-quick scheme.

8. Even while emphasizing, as we must, (**utilitarian, narcissistic**) goals, we cannot afford to ignore ethical and aesthetic values.

9. Although I had no desire to wander through a strange town on foot, I was reluctant to trust my person to the (**vagaries, rapports**) of those wild cab drivers.

10. Anyone who spends so many hours a day primping and preening in front of a mirror can only be considered a blatant (**narcissist, zealot**).

11. Every president of our country should renew our determination to create a more (**precarious, viable**) political and social structure for the future.

12. The brand new play is a brilliant (**pastiche, rapport**) of Shakespearean comedies with a focus on romantic couplings that go awry.

13. Because the speaker before me had defined the topic so narrowly, I had to revise my notes so that only (**apposite, precarious**) data remained.

14. Education is a living process that requires above all a close (**charisma, rapport**) between teacher and student.

15. What we need now is not (**utilitarian, charismatic**) leadership, however inspiring, but steady, modest, and down-to-earth assistance in defining and achieving our goals.

16. A single clown entered the ring and comically and skillfully evaded the bull; later, a collection of (**zanies, zealots**), just as comically, failed in their evasion.

17. It was in the (**execrable, penultimate**) chapter of the novel, after poring over thousands of pages, that I realized the true magnificence of the work.

18. With so many rival claimants actively engaged in trying to depose him, the monarch knew that his hold on the throne was at best (**viable, precarious**).

19. A true work of art must be an integrated whole rather than a (**vagary, pastiche**) of discrete or incongruous elements.

20. Your (**xenophobic, zealous**) enthusiasm must be matched by training and discipline if you are to achieve anything worthwhile.

21. Historians and economists fear this new gilded age might (**augur, impinge**) badly for working-class people as the gap between rich and poor widens.

22. Claire does not have last month's rent so will have to borrow the money or (**debilitate, bilk**) her landlord.

23. His idea of (**zany, zealous**) behavior at a party is to wear a lampshade as if it were a hat.

24. True patriotism is a positive attitude and is the opposite of the negative orientation of (**charisma, xenophobia**).

25. My dreams always lead me to the (**augur, labyrinth**) of a dilapidated school's hallways.

Synonyms

Choose the word from this unit that is the same or most nearly the same in meaning as the ***boldface*** *word or expression in the phrase. Write that word on the line. Use a dictionary if necessary.*

1. a **patchwork** of other people's ideas ______________________
2. **duped** the unsuspecting couple ______________________
3. subject to the **whims** of fortune ______________________
4. a disease that **enfeebles** those who contract it ______________________
5. **relevant** to the matter being discussed ______________________
6. **obtrudes** on the rights of others ______________________
7. **insipid** niceties and trite slogans ______________________
8. friends who have a unique **bond** ______________________
9. the **next-to-last** year of his life ______________________
10. criticized the politician's **chauvinism** ______________________

Antonyms

*Choose the word from this unit that is most nearly opposite in meaning to the **boldface** word or expression in the phrase. Write that word on the line. Use a dictionary if necessary.*

1. **cosmopolitan** attitude toward foreign students ____________________
2. work tirelessly to **aid** and support the elderly ____________________
3. the film's **second** scene foreshadowed ____________________
4. the commentator's **trenchant** remarks ____________________
5. **fortifying** relationship with her friends and family ____________________

Completing the Sentence

From the words in this unit, choose the one that best completes each of the following sentences. Write the word in the space provided.

1. Attacked from all sides by superior forces, the army found itself in a(n) ____________________, if not totally untenable, position.
2. We recognize the need for vigorous criticism in a political campaign, but we will certainly not tolerate that kind of ____________________ character assassination.
3. Our party can use the support of ardent young ____________________, but we also need the help of older and cooler heads.
4. Some leaders have such great personal ____________________ that they inspire an attitude akin to religious veneration in their followers.
5. Luxury and self-indulgence ____________________ the once vigorous Roman people and led to the fall of the empire.
6. It was in the ____________________ year of her life that she realized she must make amends with her daughter, and so they were able to revive a mutual feeling of tenderness.
7. "Any organization that is able to survive and prosper in these trying times has indeed proven itself ____________________," she observed.
8. As the play is essentially a(n) ____________________ of devices and ideas drawn from many different sources, it lacks the consistency and cohesiveness of the writer's other works.
9. His ____________________ remarks revealed how little he really knew about political economy.
10. When we asked the climbers why they wanted to scale the mountain, they gave the ____________________ reply, "Because it's there."

11. Only after living and working in Washington for many years were we able to find our way through the vast ____________________ of government departments and agencies.

12. Instead of sentimentalizing about the passing of rural America, we must work to achieve an effective ____________________ with our modern urban environment.

13. Their consistent attitude of hostility toward any cultural tradition different from their own cannot be excused by calling it ____________________.

14. The fumble by our quarterback on the opening drive, followed by a 15-yard penalty against us, did not ____________________ well for our team.

15. As I lay there, drifting off to sleep, suddenly the sound of a very loud, very raucous, and very obnoxious television commercial ____________________ on my ears.

16. By filing false claims over a period of many years, the pair attempted to ____________________ the insurance company of large sums of money.

17. I cannot accept a purely ____________________ view of life that ignores such aspects of human experience as beauty, love, and humor.

18. Only later did we come to realize that there was a serious purpose behind his apparently frivolous remarks and ____________________ behavior.

19. Oscar Wilde's famous epigram that "self-love is the beginning of a lifelong romance" is a clever comment on ____________________.

20. We cannot say with any confidence how long this trip will take us because our progress is dependent upon the ____________________ of the weather.

Writing: Words in Action

1. Look back at "Matriarchal Society" (pages 146–147). Imagine a modern society or government dominated by women. How would it function in the same way and/or differently as compared to a male-dominated society or government? Use this personal vision to write a compare-contrast essay, using at least two details from the passage and three unit words, in which you consider how a matriarchal society would look.

2. Some argue that women and men are inherently different, while others argue that men and women have been conditioned to assume certain roles. Do you think one point of view is more viable than the other? Or is there a middle ground? In a brief essay, support your opinion with specific examples from your studies, reading (refer to pages 146–147), or personal observations and experience. Write at least three paragraphs, and use three or more words from this unit.

Vocabulary in Context

Literary Text

The following excerpts are from Mary Wollstonecraft Shelley's novels Frankenstein *and* The Last Man. *Some of the words you have studied in this unit appear in* ***boldface*** *type. Complete each statement below the excerpt by circling the letter of the correct answer.*

1. He endeavors to fill me with hope and talks as if life were a possession which he valued ... and in spite of myself, he fills me with cheerful **auguries**. (*Frankenstein*)

Auguries are

a. curiosities **c.** omens
b. demands **d.** emotions

2. An old man sat in it, near a fire, over which he was preparing his breakfast. He turned on hearing a noise, and perceiving me, shrieked loudly, and quitting the hut, ran across the fields with a speed of which his **debilitated** form hardly appeared capable. (*Frankenstein*)

A form that is **debilitated** is NOT

a. devitalized **c.** exasperated
b. incapacitated **d.** energized

In the 1994 film adaptation of *Frankenstein*, Robert De Niro plays Frankenstein's creation.

3. We were not allowed to converse for any length of time, for the **precarious** state of my health rendered every precaution necessary that could ensure tranquility. Mr. Kirwin came in and insisted that my strength should not be exhausted by too much exertion. (*Frankenstein*)

Something **precarious** is

a. unstable **c.** robust
b. brazen **d.** false

4. Is there such a feeling as love at first sight? And if there be, in what does its nature differ from love founded in long observation and slow growth? Perhaps its effects are not so permanent; but they are, while they last, as violent and intense. We walk the pathless mazes of society ... till we hold this clue, leading us through that **labyrinth** to paradise. (*The Last Man*)

A **labyrinth** is a(n)

a. trepidation **c.** organization
b. convolution **d.** suffering

5. The **zealous** attention of Perdita claimed the first rank in the causes which induced his rapid recovery; but the second was surely the delight he felt in the ... good will of the Greeks. (*The Last Man*)

To be **zealous** is to be

a. fervent **c.** composed
b. indignant **d.** comical

Snap the code, or go to **vocabularyworkshop.com**

Vocabulary for Comprehension

*Read the following selection in which some of the words you have studied in Units 10–12 appear in **boldface** type. Then answer the questions on page 157.*

How and why do great cities develop? This passage looks at the beginnings of New York City.

(Line)

When Henry Hudson returned to Amsterdam in 1610, he informed investors that he had not found a river passage to the Pacific. But he (5) did report that he sailed into a huge, deep harbor surrounded by rich land, a **sine qua non** for a fur-trading enterprise. Dutch merchants wasted no time. They sent six ships (10) there in less than two years. Thus, the great city of New York began as a minor trading outpost in the vast Dutch mercantile empire.

For a small country, the (15) Netherlands had big plans—all bottom-line oriented. It already had holdings in Asia, Africa, and South America. For the Dutch, the New Netherlands colony, headquartered (20) at the foot of Manhattan, was a venture launched solely to make money for investors. It was managed by the Dutch West India Company. Peter Minuit arrived there to govern (25) in 1626. He quickly "bought" the island from the Native Americans for goods worth about 60 guilders.

The colony grew slowly, settled by **patricians** through a system (30) whereby land was deeded to them in return for bringing new settlers. The Dutch traded with the Native Americans, often **bilked** them, and made no effort to understand them. (35) Worse, albeit inadvertently, they passed on diseases to which the Native Americans had no resistance.

Manhattan became a cosmopolitan place, home to some (40) 2,000 people of many backgrounds and religions. But the Dutch forts were weak and no match for the four English warships that sailed into the harbor in 1664. The colony changed (45) hands, becoming the property of the Duke of York, brother of King Charles II. Changes caused by the takeover were largely **imperceptible**. The colony, now called New York, kept its (50) multicultural identity and continued to prosper. Although Dutch control lasted only forty years, its impact on the growth of New York as a commercial and cultural center is (55) undeniable.

1. In lines 1–13, the author's focus is on
   a. Manhattan's early cosmopolitan time
   b. Dutch trade with the Native Americans in the region of Manhattan
   c. the arrival of Peter Minuit in the New Netherlands colony
   d. the introduction of diseases to which Native Americans had no resistance
   e. the importance of Henry Hudson's account to the Dutch in Amsterdam

2. The meaning of **sine qua non** (line 7) is
   a. charter
   b. preference
   c. task
   d. requisite
   e. plan

3. According to the author, the key goal of the Dutch West India Company was to
   a. compile accurate coastline maps
   b. make money for its investors
   c. set up a New World colony that would compete with the Portuguese
   d. negotiate with the English
   e. explore the region for resources

4. The author's use of quotation marks around the word *bought* in line 25
   a. implies Peter Minuit acted too hastily
   b. signals this sentence is a flashback
   c. implies the transaction was not fair
   d. shows the author's reliable sources
   e. shows doubts Minuit paid for it

5. **Patricians** (line 29) most nearly means
   a. aristocrats
   b. sailors
   c. farmers
   d. commoners
   e. merchants

6. From paragraph 3 (lines 28–37), you can infer that the Dutch settlers' attitude toward Native Americans was
   a. fearful
   b. exploitative
   c. compassionate
   d. ambivalent
   e. polite

7. **Bilked** (line 33) most nearly means
   a. underestimated
   b. charmed
   c. frustrated
   d. laughed at
   e. swindled

8. Which resulted from the English takeover from the Dutch in 1664?
   a. The colony was called New York.
   b. Manhattan became a less cosmopolitan place.
   c. The fur trade declined.
   d. Closer relations were established with the Native Americans.
   e. The Dutch strengthened their forts.

9. **Imperceptible** (line 48) means
   a. obvious
   b. immediate
   c. undetectable
   d. disruptive
   e. beneficial

10. The author's attitude toward the Dutch might best be described as
   a. disdainful
   b. factual
   c. respectful
   d. apologetic
   e. ironic

11. From lines 35–37, you can infer that
   a. Europeans had no resistance to Native American diseases
   b. the Dutch spread disease to the Native Americans on purpose
   c. the Dutch, in the 1600s, wanted war against the Native Americans
   d. a greater number of Native Americans died from disease
   e. antidotes helped Native Americans

12. Which detail is NOT in the passage?
   a. England took control in 1664
   b. the Dutch headquarters were at the foot of Manhattan
   c. changes on the island after the English took over
   d. why Hudson was exploring the area
   e. why the island was named Manhattan

Two-Word Completions

Select the pair of words that best complete the meaning of each of the following passages.

1. As her ________________ lover Aeneas fled her embraces in search of his destiny on the wild and desolate shores of Italy, distraught Queen Dido ________________ herself on a huge pyre atop the highest building in Carthage.

a. apocryphal . . . bilked
b. fulsome . . . debilitated
c. apostate . . . immolated
d. execrable . . . adjudicated

2. When the representatives of labor and management found that they had reached a hopeless ________________ in the negotiations for a new contract, they called in an outside mediator to help break the deadlock and ________________ the dispute.

a. liaison . . . impinge
b. consensus . . . debilitate
c. rapport . . . dissimulate
d. impasse . . . adjudicate

3. Some anecdotes about historical figures are clearly ________________ because they contain ________________ and other improbable elements that show the stories were written at a much later date.

a. empirical . . . disparities
b. apocryphal . . . anachronisms
c. utilitarian . . . dichotomies
d. apposite . . . non sequiturs

4. Throughout the eighteenth and nineteenth centuries, the great ________________ houses of England were staffed by armies of servants and ________________, but today it is impossible for a duke or an earl to keep such a sizable domestic staff.

a. patrician . . . lackeys
b. monolithic . . . apostates
c. gothic . . . zealots
d. utilitarian . . . raconteurs

5. During your college interview, it wouldn't hurt to observe the ________________ of a formal interview while also making sure to display your skills as a(n) ________________ who is comfortable in a variety of contexts.

a. punctilios . . . raconteur
b. augurs . . . rapport
c. vagaries . . . zealot
d. non sequiturs . . . apostate

6. The gray and dreary walls of this office cubicle are far too ________________ for my wide-eyed, ________________ nature and willful disregard for authority.

a. bilking . . . fulsome
b. constricting . . . quixotic
c. debilitating . . . utilitarian
d. adjudicating . . . empirical

7. The battered war veteran taught himself to ________________ his outrage and paint wondrous, fantastical, and ________________ images that satirized the very political leaders who had led his country into war.

a. impinge . . . execrable
b. debilitate . . . penultimate
c. sublimate . . . flamboyant
d. propitiate . . . monolithic

In the passage "Matriarchal Society" (see pages 146–147), the writer points out that, in some societies, men and women live on more or less "equal footing." As a whole, this simple phrase has an altogether different meaning when compared to the literal meanings of each word examined alone.

This kind of phrase is an **idiom**. In the unit opener passage, the phrase "equal footing" means having the same status or position in society.

Choosing the Right Idiom

Read each sentence. Use context clues to figure out the meaning of each idiom in ***boldface*** *print. Then write the letter of the definition for the idiom in the sentence.*

1. Our boss says you are a bit **green around the gills**. You should go home and rest. _______
2. The weekend is over. Tomorrow is Monday, and we go **back to the salt mines**. _______
3. His analysis of the personal computing industry is **wide of the mark** and doesn't impress me. _______
4. **In one fell swoop**, the child stepped on the dog's tail, pulled down the bookshelf, and broke the radio. _______
5. The restaurant manager left her job **under a cloud**, as she was accused of mishandling funds. _______
6. The mayor is using this issue as a **red herring** to divert attention from the teachers' strike. _______
7. The school's organic garden was a **labor of love** that took five full years to realize. _______
8. Mr. Lee is overconfident and tends to forget that he is only a **big fish in a small pond**. _______
9. Because I trust you completely, I will give you **free rein** to develop and manage the project to the end. _______
10. After the statement, the press secretary had to answer the journalists' questions **off the cuff**. _______

a. off target

b. something that distracts or misleads

c. most important person in a small group

d. sickly looking

e. complete freedom

f. all at once

g. without planning

h. something done only for the satisfaction

i. time to return to something unpleasant, such as work

j. under suspicion

Writing with Idioms

Find the meaning of each idiom. (Use an online or print dictionary if necessary.) Then write a sentence for each idiom.

1. fly in the ointment

2. water under the bridge

3. a stone's throw

4. at a loss

5. take the fall

6. cook the books

7. tall order

8. set the world on fire

9. against the grain

10. drop the ball

11. keep it under your hat

12. raw deal

Denotation and Connotation

Words have both literal meanings, or **denotations**, and informal or implied meanings. These typically numerous and subjective meanings are called **connotations**. Readers or listeners bring connotations—positive, negative, or neutral—to words, while they look up the words' denotations in the dictionary.

For example, consider these synonyms a writer might use for the neutral word *leave: desert, withdraw, retreat, vacate, abandon,* or *flee*. Each word conveys a different meaning. Excellent writers and speakers choose words carefully in order to refine their work and make it richer in meaning.

Consider these synonyms for the neutral word *impasse*:

standoff *dead end* *deadlock* *stalemate*

Standoff might have a more positive connotation, suggesting that the two parties in question could still come to an agreement. In contrast, *dead end* implies that there is no hope at all for agreement. While slightly more positive than *dead end*, *deadlock* and *stalemate* are still relatively negative and suggest little hope for progress.

Think: A political standoff could possibly result in a compromise, while a political stalemate often lasts for an indefinite period of time and has no positive result.

Look at these examples of words that are similar in denotation but have different connotations.

NEUTRAL	POSITIVE	NEGATIVE
hide	**pretend**	**dissimulate**
predicament	**mix-up**	**quagmire**
dispute	**squabble**	**vendetta**

Skillfully understanding and using a word's denotation and its connotations are important ways to get the most out of what you read and to perfect your writing.

Shades of Meaning

Write a plus sign (+) in the box if the word has a positive connotation. Write a minus sign (–) if the word has a negative connotation. Put a zero (0) if the word is neutral.

1. sine qua non ☐ **2.** acumen ☐ **3.** fulsome ☐ **4.** immolate ☐

5. consensus ☐ **6.** nihilism ☐ **7.** bilk ☐ **8.** anachronism ☐

9. charisma ☐ **10.** execrable ☐ **11.** narcissism ☐ **12.** zany ☐

13. xenophobia ☐ **14.** augur ☐ **15.** penultimate ☐ **16.** debilitate ☐

Expressing the Connotation

Read each sentence. Select the word in parentheses that expresses the connotation (positive, negative, or neutral) given at the beginning of the sentence.

negative 1. The (**unintelligent, vacuous**) culture of consumption has had a deleterious effect on youth today.

neutral 2. Will the recent court ruling (**affect, impinge on**) our everyday rights and freedoms?

neutral 3. After the tornado destroyed her home, my best friend was in a (**precarious, perilous**) state.

negative 4. Your neighbor is a political (**bigot, zealot**) who cannot accept that others have a different view of the future.

positive 5. Her team produced an economically thrifty and (**viable, possible**) plan for rebuilding the bridge.

neutral 6. The climbers' situation became (**parlous, uncertain**) as the storm unleashed its power.

neutral 7. Cuts in college loans to struggling families will certainly (**constrict, strangle**) their economic futures.

negative 8. Her accounts of a heroic and accomplished ancestry are most certainly (**fraudulent, apocryphal**).

Challenge: Using Connotation

Choose vocabulary words from Units 10–12 to replace the highlighted words in the sentences below. Then explain how the connotation of the replacement word changes the tone of the sentence.

disparity	**euphoria**	**effusive**
flamboyant	**gothic**	**lugubrious**

1. Their grandparents arrived—bearing an abundance of gifts—and the children's **delight** ____________________ was palpable.

____

____

2. Jenny's **mawkish** ____________________ gratitude surprised everyone at the farewell party.

____

3. The nurse's **downcast** ____________________ eyes helped me understand that my grandfather's health was declining.

____

____

Classical Roots

chron—time

This Greek root appears in **anachronism** (page 128), which means "a misplacing in time of events, objects, customs, or persons in regard to each other." Some other words based on the same root are listed below.

chronically	**chronicler**	**chronology**	**crony**
chronicle	**chronological**	**chronometer**	**cronyism**

From the list of words above, choose the one that corresponds to each of the brief definitions below. Write the word in the blank space in the illustrative sentence below the definition.

1. an exceptionally accurate clock, watch, or other timepiece

The marine biologist especially values her underwater ____________________ when she dives.

2. the determination of dates or of the sequence of events; the sequential ordering of dates and events; such a list or table

The documentary provides an accurate ____________________ of key battles of the last century.

3. one who writes or keeps a record of historical events

That magazine has long been regarded as an astute ____________________ of fashion.

4. arranged in order of time or occurrence; relating to or in keeping with the ordering of events in time

This discography is a ____________________ listing of all of the composer's recorded works.

5. a record of historical events presented in order of occurrence; to make or keep such a record

Anne Frank's poignant ____________________ of her years in hiding in an Amsterdam attic during World War II has been translated into scores of languages.

6. favoritism shown to old friends or companions in official or political appointments

The search committee accused the dean of ____________________ in his recent appointments.

7. a close friend or companion, chum

They planned an outing at the beach as a casual reunion of their old school

____________________.

8. constantly, habitually, over a prolonged period

Despite his responsibility as recording secretary, he is ____________________ late for meetings.

UNIT 13

*Read the following selection, taking note of the **boldface** words and their contexts. These words are among those you will be studying in Unit 13. As you complete the exercises in this unit, it may help to refer to the way the words are used below.*

Time to Clean Up Space

<Newspaper Editorial>

An artist's conception of space junk

In March 2009, when the crew of the $100 billion International Space Station was forced to implement emergency **protocols** for fleeing in an escape vehicle, the threat they sought to evade was posed not by a rogue state or an alien starship, but by a five-inch chunk of space junk. Had the debris actually struck the station, it might have depleted its entire oxygen supply. Fortunately, it missed.

We tend to think of space as **immaculate**, wide-open, and **resplendent** in its emptiness. We're proud, to the point of **vainglory**, about our extraterrestrial accomplishments, heaping **accolades** on brave astronauts and brilliant rocket scientists. But our efforts in space are **stigmatized** due to our lamentable failure to clean up after ourselves out there. As a result, a giant cloud of space junk—old rocket boosters, **vestiges** of satellites, implements discarded by astronauts, fragmentary traces of bygone collisions—now circles the planet. And this swirling junkyard poses a **chronic** threat to spacecraft, to astronauts, and to the communications satellites that our technologically-driven society has come to depend on.

In decades past, scientists treated space junk as a minor nuisance; many were convinced that debris in Earth's orbit would soon wear itself down by **attrition** and fall harmlessly back to the planet, burnt up by the atmosphere. As it turns out, most space junk is likely to remain in orbit for thousands, even millions, of years. As we live, so we learn: NASA now tracks 11,000 large items of space junk, and the number is rising steadily. If nothing is done to check the increasing quantity of space junk, the risk of collision could eventually become so severe as to make space missions impracticable, perhaps permanently grounding all the world's space programs.

Thankfully, the problem is not **ineluctable**, and a range of solutions is available to address it. To begin with, spacefaring nations should come together, under their own **volition**, to develop global policies for managing space junk and producing less of it. For example, all nations should agree to a moratorium on secret tests of anti-missile weapons, as these **sub rosa** experiments and the explosions they cause in space significantly increase the volume of junk in orbit. Political agreements won't come easily, but there are good reasons to hope that relevant nations might overcome **chauvinist** bias and **factionalism** to make a deal: The growing threat from space junk is something all spacefaring nations have in common, and the threat to communications satellites should make a political solution universally appealing, at least in principle.

Technical solutions must also be tried. Robots could install rockets on dead spacecraft to knock them out of orbit and send them soaring back to Earth; powerful lasers could be used to zap smaller items of debris into oblivion. Unfortunately, as many scientists note with **acerbity**, these solutions are barely feasible today and would require significant and steady funding at a time when government support for space programs is already far too scarce and **mercurial**.

Until all the orbiting junk is cleared from the heavens, designers of spacecraft must combat space debris the old-fashioned way—by providing extra layers of protective cladding, or coating. Unfortunately, the added bulk makes satellites and vehicles heavier and far more costly. And while defensive measures like these might **palliate** matters, they do nothing to address the underlying problem. There's only one way to do that: Get the junk out of orbit.

iWords™

Snap the code, or go to **vocabularyworkshop.com**

Debris from Space Shuttle Columbia is found in the field of a family home in Texas, 2003.

Computer artwork of space debris

Note the spelling, pronunciation, part(s) of speech, and definition(s) of each of the following words. Then write the word in the blank spaces in the illustrative sentence(s) following. Finally, study the lists of synonyms and antonyms.

1. accolade (ak′ ə lād)

(*n.*) praise or approval; a ceremonial embrace or greeting

The playwright enjoyed the ____________________ of both the theater critics and the public.

SYNONYMS: kudos, acclaim, cheers, plaudits
ANTONYMS: boos, disapproval, censure

2. acerbity (ə sər′ bə tē)

(*n.*) sourness or bitterness of taste; harshness or severity of manner or expression

Offended by the ____________________ of the director's remarks, the actor stormed out of the rehearsal.

SYNONYMS: acidity, astringency, mordancy, asperity
ANTONYMS: blandness, mellowness, mildness

3. attrition (ə trish′ ən)

(*n.*) the process of wearing down by friction or gradual impairment

After many losses due to ____________________, the weakened army sought an end to hostilities.

SYNONYMS: abrasion, erosion, reduction
ANTONYMS: augmentation, proliferation, enlargement

4. bromide (brō′ mīd)

(*n.*) a trite or commonplace remark; a tiresome or boring person; a sedative

The usual ____________________ offered by politicians may please crowds but won't solve the nation's problems.

SYNONYM: platitude

5. chauvinist (shō′ və nist)

(*adj.*) extravagantly patriotic; blindly devoted to a cause; (*n.*) such a person

During wartime, some newspapers may take an extremely ____________________ stance in their editorials.

Denying that he is a male ____________________, the senator cited his record of support for equal rights for women.

SYNONYMS: (*n.*) superpatriot, flag-waver, jingoist

6. chronic (kron′ ik)

(*adj.*) continuing over a long period of time or recurring often

The president set up a blue-ribbon committee to look into the problem of ____________________ unemployment.

SYNONYMS: recurrent, persistent, inveterate, habitual
ANTONYMS: transitory, transient, sporadic

7. expound
(ek spaůnd')

(*v.*) to explain in detail

The students listened attentively as their physics professor ____________ upon the new theory.

SYNONYMS: elucidate, delineate

8. factionalism
(fak' shən əl iz əm)

(*n.*) party strife and intrigue

Because of bitter ____________ in both houses of Congress, no legislation of consequence was passed.

SYNONYM: infighting
ANTONYMS: unanimity, harmony, agreement, consensus

9. immaculate
(i mak' yə lit)

(*adj.*) spotless; without blemish or fault

After I finished washing and waxing my parents' white car, it was as ____________ as new-fallen snow.

SYNONYM: unsoiled
ANTONYMS: blemished, tarnished, stained, sullied

10. imprecation
(im prə kā' shən)

(*n.*) a curse; the act of cursing

When I found myself stuck in a traffic jam, I could not resist muttering a few ____________.

SYNONYM: execration
ANTONYM: benediction

11. ineluctable
(in i lək' tə bəl)

(*adj.*) not able to be avoided, changed, or overcome

Two of life's ____________ facts are death and taxes.

SYNONYMS: unavoidable, inevitable
ANTONYMS: avoidable, escapable, reversible, revocable

12. mercurial
(mər kyůr' ē əl)

(*adj.*) characterized by rapid and unpredictable changes of mood; fickle or inconstant

The temperamental diva is perhaps even more famous for her ____________ behavior than for her voice.

SYNONYMS: erratic, capricious, volatile
ANTONYMS: phlegmatic, sluggish, constant, steady

13. palliate
(pal' ē āt)

(*v.*) to make less serious or severe by glossing over; to relieve without actually curing, mitigate

A few new laws may ____________ the ills that plague our society but will not eradicate them.

SYNONYMS: alleviate, extenuate
ANTONYMS: intensify, magnify, aggravate

14. protocol (prō′ tə kôl)

(*n.*) customs and regulations dealing with official behavior and etiquette, as in a court or among diplomats; a type of international agreement; a memorandum, official account, or record

A breach of ____________________ at a summit meeting of world leaders can have serious consequences.

SYNONYMS: code of conduct, minutes

15. resplendent (ri splen′ dənt)

(*adj.*) shining or gleaming brilliantly; splendid or magnificent

The knights, clad in ____________________ armor, rode forth to engage the foe.

SYNONYMS: radiant, dazzling, glorious; ANTONYMS: dull, lusterless

16. stigmatize (stig′ mə tīz)

(*v.*) to brand or mark as in some way discreditable, disgraceful, or ignominious

People sometimes ____________________ innocent children because of their parents' misdeeds.

SYNONYMS: sully, taint; ANTONYMS: whitewash, laud, extol

17. sub rosa (səb rō′ zə)

(*adv.*) in secret; confidentially; privately; (*adj.*) secretive

An unnamed White House source passed crucial information to reporters ____________________.

At a series of ____________________ meetings, the dissenting shareholders planned their next move.

SYNONYMS: (*adv.*) secretly, covertly, stealthily, furtively
ANTONYMS: (*adv.*) overtly, openly

18. vainglory (vān′ glô rē)

(*n.*) excessive pride in and boastfulness about one's own accomplishments or qualities; a vain show or display

With insufferable ____________________ the young tennis star taunted his opponent after each winning point.

SYNONYMS: vanity, conceit, swagger, pretentiousness
ANTONYMS: humility, modesty, diffidence

19. vestige (ves′ tij)

(*n.*) a trace or visible evidence of something that once existed but now is lost or vanished

The spectacular ruins of the ancient temple are the last ____________________ of a once-mighty civilization.

SYNONYMS: artifact, remains

20. volition (vō lish′ ən)

(*n.*) the power to choose, will, or decide; the act of choosing, willing, or deciding

Ignoring all my relatives' warnings, I chose the perilous course of my own ____________________.

SYNONYMS: free will, choice
ANTONYMS: coercion, compulsion, duress

Choosing the Right Word

*Select the **boldface** word that better completes each sentence. You might refer to the selection on pages 164–165 to see how most of these words are used in context.*

1. His claim to be the "greatest pole-vaulter in the world" would indeed have seemed outrageously (**sub rosa, vainglorious**) if it were not for the fact that he went ahead and proved it.

2. George Washington's (**immaculate, mercurial**) reputation as a dedicated patriot has been an inspiration to many generations of Americans.

3. We sought desperately for some new forms of amusement to (**palliate, expound**) the boredom of those endless summer afternoons.

4. Our party can resist the attacks of its enemies from the outside, but it may fall victim to the erosion of (**bromide, factionalism**) from within.

Pole-vaulting has been a sport since the mid-nineteenth century.

5. Because the difficulty of the subject matter increases rapidly as the term proceeds, mathematics and physics courses have a high rate of student (**attrition, vainglory**).

6. We spent most of the evening listening to her (**palliate, expound**) on her views on all sorts of interesting subjects.

7. Letting the grim facts speak for themselves, the doctor explained quietly the (**ineluctable, immaculate**) tragedy that results from drug abuse.

8. My brother's (**chronic, resplendent**) tardiness is perpetually getting him into trouble at school.

9. Beneath the (**volition, acerbity**) of their criticism, we recognized a sincere desire to help us solve our problems.

10. Critics who bestow their (**stigma, accolades**) too easily may gain some quick popularity, but they will soon lose their credibility and influence.

11. His talents, which had seemed so (**vestigial, resplendent**) in his youth, now struck us as unimpressive and even pathetic.

12. Your threats and (**imprecations, protocols**) leave me unimpressed because I know that your words will not be followed by deeds.

13. Though they are twins, one of them has a highly (**mercurial, vestigial**) temperament, while the other is stolid and reserved.

14. "My country, right or wrong" expresses (**chauvinism, attrition**) in its most common form.

15. They preceded her to the table, not because (**volition, protocol**) required it, but because they were eager to get at the food.

16. The small bone at the base of the spinal column in humans is thought by biologists to be the (**vestige, accolade**) of a tail.

17. Although he saw himself as a wit, a bon vivant, and a man-about-town, everyone else regarded him as a hopeless (**factionalism, bromide**).

18. We are all eager to avoid the (**accolade, stigma**) of being prejudiced and, perhaps, simultaneously unwilling to purge ourselves of our biases.

19. In the light of the lessons of history, I am skeptical about the value of any diplomatic conferences held (**sub rosa, ineluctably**).

20. Although she emphasizes that she was the helpless victim of bad luck, one can recognize the effects of her own (**imprecation, volition**) in bringing about her downfall.

21. It was not until she entered the workforce in her small town in the 1950s that she realized the preponderance of male (**factionalists, chauvinists**) in positions of power.

22. My supervisor was uncomfortable with the (**ineluctable, sub rosa**) meetings held in order to determine which departments would be dissolved.

23. Your (**bromides, accolades**) neither assure me nor enlighten me, and, in fact, I would like you to keep your hackneyed advice to yourself.

24. The distinctive (**acerbity, attrition**) of the choke cherries did not prevent the girl from eating at least one for every two she placed in her pail.

25. The computer technician configured a revised (**protocol, volition**) to access new mail.

Synonyms

*Choose the word from this unit that is the same or most nearly the same in meaning as the **boldface** word or expression in the phrase. Write that word on the line. Use a dictionary if necessary.*

1. preserved the **relics** of an ancient culture ______________
2. used one **cliché** after another ______________
3. a tirade filled with **maledictions** ______________
4. **disgraced** because of past mistakes ______________
5. an **impeccable** record of service ______________
6. asked to **explicate** the meaning of the poem ______________
7. an organization riven by **dissension** ______________
8. known as a **flighty** individual ______________
9. ranks depleted by **exhaustion** ______________
10. the **inescapable** ravages of time ______________

Antonyms

*Choose the word from this unit that is most nearly opposite in meaning to the **boldface** word or expression in the phrase. Write that word on the line. Use a dictionary if necessary.*

1. the judge **refrained from comment** on the case ____________________
2. accepted the **criticism** with good grace ____________________
3. the orator delivered **blessings** to passersby ____________________
4. the great value of his **original wit** ____________________
5. clad in **drab** garments ____________________

Completing the Sentence

From the words in this unit, choose the one that best completes each of the following sentences. Write the word in the space provided.

1. ____________________ in her first evening gown and her first professional hairdo, she waited impatiently for her date to escort her to the dance.

2. In the innocent glow of youth and inexperience, we simply assumed that we would be able to avoid the ____________________ consequences of our own folly.

3. Many a time-honored home remedy may indeed ____________________ the symptoms of a disease but do little or nothing to cure it.

4. Over the years she has tried many different remedies to relieve the pain caused by her____________________ arthritis.

5. G. B. Shaw's remark to the effect that "youth is wasted on the young" may be, as you say, an old ____________________, but it is also profoundly true.

6. The agreements that had been concluded ____________________ by the leaders of both parties aroused a storm of protest when they were finally made public.

7. No one suggested that I take an art class in my freshman year; I decided to do it purely of my own ____________________.

8. Since we cannot overcome the enemy by direct attack, we will wage a war of ____________________ against them.

9. Why is it that so many theater critics are noted for the trenchancy of their perceptions and the ____________________ of their wit?

10. It was a bitter experience to have to leave the village in disgrace, followed by the jeers and ____________________ of people I had tried to help.

11. In an influential book published in 1936, the economist John M. Keynes ____________________ his theory of the causes of economic collapse.

12. In spite of her advanced age and illness, one could still recognize the ____________________ of her once ravishing beauty.

13. Have we reached the stage where anyone who refuses to go along with the majority is to be ____________________ as a malcontent?

14. Shall I be modest and say that I simply do not deserve these extravagant ____________________, or shall I be honest and admit that I do?

15. His personality was so ____________________ that we never knew on any given occasion how he would react.

16. The Founding Fathers warned that without an overriding sense of national purpose, this country could be torn apart by ____________________.

17. Despite the heat and the dirt of a summer day in the city, he managed somehow to look cool and ____________________.

18. The steady and quiet devotion of people who truly love their country is very different from the noisy fulminations of mindless ____________________.

19. You may be scornful about matters of "mere ____________________," as you call it, but you will soon learn that *how* things are done is often as important as *what* is done.

20. Isn't there truly an element of pathos in the certain knowledge that the ____________________ and overconfidence of our youth will be laid low by "the slings and arrows of outrageous fortune"?

Writing: Words in Action

1. Look back at "Time to Clean Up Space" (pages 164–165). Imagine you are a NASA representative testifying before the U.S. Congress. Write a prepared statement in which you attempt to convince the government to fund a program to eradicate debris, or "space junk," in orbit around Earth. Use at least three details from the passage and three unit words in your essay.

2. Some scientists estimate that there are approximately 6.4 million tons of plastic debris swirling in Earth's oceans. Do you think cleaning up pollution on Earth and in space have the same level of urgency? Write a compare-contrast essay of at least three paragraphs, and use three or more words from this unit, in which you consider the urgency of pollution on land, in the oceans, and in space. Use specific examples from your studies, reading (refer to pages 164–165), or personal observations and experience.

Vocabulary in Context

Literary Text

The following excerpts are from Nathaniel Hawthorne's novels The Scarlet Letter *and* The House of the Seven Gables. *Some of the words you have studied in this unit appear in* ***boldface*** *type. Complete each statement below the excerpt by circling the letter of the correct answer.*

1. The young clergyman, after a few hours of privacy, was sensible that the disorder of his nerves had hurried him into an unseemly outbreak of temper, which there had been nothing in the physician's words to excuse or **palliate**. (*The Scarlet Letter*)

To **palliate** is to

a. explain
b. exacerbate
c. ease
d. prescribe

2. She assumed a freedom of speculation, then common enough on the other side of the Atlantic, but which our forefathers, had they known it, would have held to be a deadlier crime than that **stigmatized** by the scarlet letter. (*The Scarlet Letter*)

Something that is **stigmatized** is

a. tarnished
b. purloined
c. provoked
d. acclaimed

Hester Prynne and her daughter, Pearl, in *The Scarlet Letter*

3. Deeper it goes, and deeper into the wilderness, less plainly to be seen at every step; until some few miles hence the yellow leaves will show no **vestige** of the white man's tread. There thou art free! (*The Scarlet Letter*)

A **vestige** is a(n)

a. tribute
b. outfit
c. magnificence
d. indication

4. It was quite otherwise with Hepzibah; the Judge's smile seemed to operate on her **acerbity** of heart like sunshine upon vinegar, making it ten times sourer than ever. (*The House of the Seven Gables*)

Acerbity is NOT

a. bitterness
b. tenderness
c. intelligence
d. capriciousness

5. In fact, entirely as she loved him, Hepzibah could hardly have borne any longer the wretched duty—so impracticable by her few and rigid faculties—of seeking pastime for a still sensitive, but ruined mind, critical and fastidious, without force or **volition**. (*The House of the Seven Gables*)

Without **volition** is without

a. emotion
b. understanding
c. will
d. hope

Snap the code, or go to **vocabularyworkshop.com**

*Read the following selection, taking note of the **boldface** words and their contexts. These words are among those you will be studying in Unit 14. As you complete the exercises in this unit, it may help to refer to the way the words are used below.*

A Gap Year Makes Sense

<Persuasive Essay>

This year, over two million American high school seniors will pack up laptops, smart phones, and other sundry **accoutrements** of teenage life and head off to college. Their reasons for going may be **unimpeachable**: to follow academic interests, to gain new skills, to prepare for careers. But is it possible they're in too much of a hurry? The fact is, over one-third will drop out after just one year of college. These **truncated** college careers represent a loss to the students themselves, to their colleges, and to the nation as a whole. One way to help avoid this outcome, according to an increasing number of students and educators, is to take a year off from school after high school graduation. This year has come to be known as the gap year.

Many college students start out full of optimism and enthusiasm, but any of a wide range of **disparate** factors can **supervene** to knock them off course. Some students discover they're not in the right program or school. Others, after four years of diligent work in high school, fail to apply themselves when they get to college, inclined instead to explore their new-found freedom. Insufficient preparation for college-level work, financial concerns, homesickness —the list is long, and each story is ultimately unique. But whatever the reason, dropping out of college is more than a minor **contretemps**. Many who leave regret their choice for years to come; some are burdened with student loans that they can hardly repay. And think of all the hours spent **bickering** with disillusioned parents...

Today's college-bound students report extremely high levels of stress. The most ambitious are likely to have been burning the candle at both ends, under pressure to get good grades and excel at multiple extracurricular pursuits while maintaining satisfying social lives. In such

circumstances, a year off from school and a chance to revitalize oneself might seem especially **apropos**.

A gap year also affords young people more time to mature—particularly when that time is spent productively. Interning at an office or volunteering at a local charity can provide real-life experience and broaden horizons. Working at a job has similar effects, and the income earned can be **meted** out to defray next year's tuition. Travel abroad, wilderness survival camp, exchange programs, volunteer work in a **populous** developing nation—there are many programs specifically designed to enrich the experience, confidence, and credentials of students "in the gap."

Productive "gappers" thus have an opportunity to practice self-reliance, gain self-awareness, and see how the world works outside the classroom. In the process, their gap-year experiences are likely to **coalesce** into insight that can help them **cull** their often confused notions about colleges, careers, and their skills and enable them to make wiser decisions once they return to school.

Many parents and some educators remain adamantly opposed to the gap year and decry its allegedly **noxious** effects. Their **polemics** typically rest on the claim that a single year off will inevitably expand into two or three, increasing the gapper's risk of being derailed from the college track. Happily, this concern is not generally borne out by the facts: Research demonstrates that most high-school grads who plan to go to college after a year off actually do go back to school once that year is up.

Statistics aside, the decision to take or not to take a year off before college should be approached with deliberation and **probity**, with no illusions about the character and circumstances of each student. There's no room for **dogmatic** arguments here. But there's little doubt that, for a great many college-bound high-school graduates, a gap year can provide opportunities for growth that are more likely to increase than to decrease the odds of subsequent success.

iWords™

Snap the code, or go to **vocabularyworkshop.com**

Above: Students volunteer in a building project.

Left, top: Some students find teaching overseas rewarding.

Left, bottom: A volunteer in Ghana

Definitions

Note the spelling, pronunciation, part(s) of speech, and definition(s) of each of the following words. Then write the word in the blank spaces in the illustrative sentence(s) following. Finally, study the lists of synonyms and antonyms.

1. accoutrements (ə kü′ trə mənts)

(*n., pl.*) accessory items of clothing or equipment; a soldier's outfit, usually not including arms or clothing; trappings

When the new administration took office, it was accorded all the ____________________ of power.

SYNONYMS: gear, equipage, appurtenances

2. apogee (ap′ ə jē)

(*n.*) the point in the orbit of a heavenly body or artificial satellite farthest from Earth; the farthest or highest point

Many people consider the works of Michelangelo to represent the ____________________ of Renaissance art.

SYNONYMS: apex, summit, pinnacle
ANTONYMS: bottom, pits, perigee

3. apropos (ap rə pō′)

(*adj.*) appropriate, opportune; (*adv.*) relevantly; incidentally, by the way; speaking of

When choosing a greeting card, I look for the one that is most ____________________ to the occasion.

____________________ of your plans for the summer, where are you going to spend your vacation?

SYNONYMS: (*adj.*) pertinent, germane, apposite, relevant
ANTONYMS: (*adj.*) irrelevant, inappropriate, immaterial

4. bicker (bik′ ər)

(*v.*) to engage in a petty or peevish dispute; to move or run rapidly, rush; to flicker, quiver

If we ____________________ over every minor detail, we'll never get the job done.

SYNONYMS: wrangle, quarrel
ANTONYMS: concur, agree, acquiesce

5. coalesce (kō ə les′)

(*v.*) to blend together or fuse so as to form one body or substance

Many small tributaries ____________________ to form the mighty Amazon River.

SYNONYMS: amalgamate, merge, combine, unite
ANTONYMS: scatter, diffuse, separate

6. contretemps (kon′ trə tän)

(*n.*) an inopportune or embarrassing occurrence; a mishap

I believe in taking life's ____________________ in stride rather than making a fuss over them.

SYNONYMS: blunder, mischance, faux pas, gaffe

7. convolution (kon və lü′ shən)

(*n.*) a rolling up, coiling, or twisting together; a sinuous folding or design

Becase of its many ____________________, San Francisco's Lombard Street is called "the crookedest street in the world."

SYNONYMS: twist, turn

8. cull (kəl)

(*v.*) to pick out or select; to gather or collect

I will ____________________ pertinent quotations from my research to illustrate the point of my paper.

SYNONYMS: choose, pluck

9. disparate (dis par′ ət) *or* (dis′ pər it)

(*adj.*) completely distinct or different; entirely dissimilar

Despite our ____________________ backgrounds and life experiences, we have remained the best of friends.

SYNONYM: divergent
ANTONYMS: similar, homogeneous, uniform

10. dogmatic (dôg mat′ ik)

(*adj.*) certain of the truth of one's own ideas; inclined to state opinions as if they were indisputable facts

People who are ____________________ are unlikely to have much tolerance for views that differ from their own.

SYNONYMS: opinionated, doctrinaire, authoritarian
ANTONYMS: open-minded, disinterested, dispassionate

11. licentious (lī sen′ shəs)

(*adj.*) morally or sexually unrestrained; having no regard for accepted rules, customs, or laws

In *The Lives of the Caesars* the biographer Suetonius describes the emperor Caligula's ____________________ behavior.

SYNONYMS: dissolute, lascivious
ANTONYMS: modest, restrained, prudish

12. mete (mēt)

(*v.*) to distribute or apportion by or as if by measure; to allot

Part of the job of being a parent is the responsibility to ____________________ out suitable punishment when a child misbehaves.

SYNONYMS: assign, parcel out

13. noxious (nok′ shəs)

(*adj.*) harmful to physical health or morals

Firefighters wear respirator masks to protect them from smoke and ____________________ fumes.

SYNONYMS: pernicious, noisome, deleterious
ANTONYMS: wholesome, salubrious, beneficial

14. polemic
(pə lem′ ik)

(*n.*) an aggressive attack on or refutation of a specific opinion or doctrine

The columnist was known for his ________________ against those at the opposite end of the political spectrum.

SYNONYMS: diatribe, controversy

15. populous
(pop′ yə ləs)

(*adj.*) full of people; filled to capacity; densely populated; having a large population

Millions of people along the ________________ Atlantic Coast fled inland as the hurricane approached.

SYNONYMS: crowded, teeming, swarming
ANTONYMS: uninhabited, unpeopled, deserted, barren

16. probity
(prō′ bə tē)

(*n.*) complete and confirmed honesty; total integrity

We should demand that our elected officals conduct themselves with the utmost ________________.

SYNONYM: uprightness
ANTONYMS: corruption, venality, immorality, iniquity

17. repartee
(rep ər tē′)

(*n.*) a swift, witty reply; conversation full of such remarks; skill in making such replies or conversation

The writers who made up the famous Algonquin Roundtable were celebrated for their sparkling ________________.

SYNONYMS: retort, comeback, banter

18. supervene
(sü pər vēn′)

(*v.*) to take place or occur as something additional or unexpected; to follow immediately after

Events that none of us could have foreseen in our wildest imaginings ________________ to blight our hopes.

SYNONYM: succeed
ANTONYMS: precede, antecede

19. truncate
(trən′ kāt)

(*v.*) to shorten by or as if by cutting off, lop

A family emergency forced us to ________________ our summer vacation.

SYNONYMS: trim, abbreviate
ANTONYMS: lengthen, elongate, extend, protract

20. unimpeachable
(ən im pē′ chə bəl)

(*adj.*) beyond doubt or reproach; unquestionable

The members of the jury found the testimony of the key prosecution witness to be ________________.

SYNONYMS: irreproachable, irrefutable, unassailable
ANTONYMS: debatable, dubious

Choosing the Right Word

*Select the **boldface** word that better completes each sentence. You might refer to the selection on pages 174–175 to see how most of these words are used in context.*

White-tailed deer are commonly seen in North America and often form herds in the winter months.

1. The decision by the local government to (**supervene, cull**) the white-tailed deer population this autumn is controversial and has incited protests from many groups.

2. Because the original article was too long for our needs, we published it in a somewhat (**coalesced, truncated**) form.

3. We must not close our eyes to the flagrant (**disparities, contretemps**) between what our society aspires to be and what it actually is.

4. How do you expect to deal with the inevitable problems of life if you raise every (**repartee, contretemps**) to the level of a major tragedy?

5. The reporter assured her boss that the charges contained in her story were based on information from a(n) (**unimpeachable, noxious**) source.

6. We expected a simple explanation, but what we got was an involved rationalization, full of all kinds of strange (**contretemps, convolutions**).

7. Even the most relentless investigations by our political opponents could uncover no evidence that challenged our reputation for (**dogmatism, probity**).

8. "Unless the various factions put aside their differences and (**coalesce, supervene**) into a unified force, we will get absolutely nowhere," I said.

9. I agree that it is a very good book, but it is a gross exaggeration to say that it represents the (**apogee, convolution**) of the development of the American novel.

10. What they described as a new spirit of freedom and vigorous originality seemed to me mere (**accoutrements, licentiousness**).

11. I have neither the time nor the inclination to plough through those long, dreary books in the hope of (**meting, culling**) a few interesting passages.

12. If you are to get along in polite society, you must learn that a remark that is factually true is not necessarily (**populous, apropos**).

13. When we least expected it, a crucial event (**coalesced, supervened**) that changed the outcome of our project.

14. I had hoped for some understanding and generosity of spirit, not this endless (**bickering, repartee**) over petty details.

15. Instead of taking a fresh look at the situation, they were satisfied to refute their opponents by repeating old and weary (**polemics, accoutrements**).

16. Los Angeles supplanted Chicago as the second most (**populous, unimpeachable**) city in the United States.

17. (**Repartee, Supervention**) has been likened to a sort of verbal fencing, with the more skillful contestants driving home their weapons for the kill.

18. We are all imperfect creatures, and none of us has been divinely ordained to (**cull, mete**) out punishment to others for their transgressions.

19. The route of the army's retreat was littered with the discarded (**polemics, accoutrements**) of war.

20. From the roots of ancient prejudices, there grew the (**disparate, noxious**) plants of racial and religious hatreds.

21. After a long silence, and when everyone was sufficiently uncomfortable, she announced, (**accoutrements, apropos**) of nothing, that they were to be married the next weekend.

22. Abraham Lincoln warned that the (**convolutions, dogmas**) of the quiet past were inadequate to the needs of the stormy present.

23. The last hours of the roadtrip required no soundtrack, as the three small children (**bickered, supervened**) so incessantly that not even a passing firetruck could be heard.

24. Unfortunately, there will always be a lawmaker accused of (**unimpeachable, licentious**) conduct, and there will always be a journalist happy to report endlessly on it.

25. Mathematicians and students (**mete, truncate**) the infinite digits of *pi* to 3.14.

*Choose the word from this unit that is the same or most nearly the same in meaning as the **boldface** word or expression in the phrase. Write that word on the line. Use a dictionary if necessary.*

1. reached its **zenith** and then descended ____________
2. earned them a reputation for **rectitude** ____________
3. began to **squabble** as soon as we sat down ____________
4. unprepared for the disaster that **ensued** ____________
5. disgusted by their **wanton** behavior ____________
6. amused by their **verbal sparring** ____________
7. **gleaned** a few key ideas from the article ____________
8. forced to **curtail** their stay ____________
9. the **toxic** effects of air pollution ____________
10. one unexpected **complication** after another ____________

Antonyms

*Choose the word from this unit that is most nearly opposite in meaning to the **boldface** word or expression in the phrase. Write that word on the line. Use a dictionary if necessary.*

1. a person of **questionable** character ____________________
2. dreadfully **dull dialogue** in the film ____________________
3. the **nadir** of the president's popularity rating ____________________
4. the **simplicity** and sincerity of her argument ____________________
5. a **chaste** and comforting embrace ____________________

Completing the Sentence

From the words in this unit, choose the one that best completes each of the following sentences. Write the word in the space provided.

1. I hate to ____________________ with you over the cost of a few gallons of gasoline, but I have to because I don't have a dime to spare.

2. The report was not an impartial assessment of the problems we face; it was an intemperate ____________________.

3. Although the premier enjoyed all the ____________________ of high office, in practice he was merely a figurehead who wielded very little power.

4. Does "artistic freedom" justify the making of a movie that is deliberately vulgar and ____________________ in the hope of cashing in at the box office?

5. From the vast mass of unsolicited manuscripts, the editor ____________________ the few that might be considered for publication.

6. It was absolutely impossible to follow the ____________________ of the man's tortuous reasoning as he desperately tried to prove his point.

7. Five minutes after arriving at the dance, I upset the punch bowl—the first of many ____________________ that made the evening a nightmare.

8. Their respective talents seemed to ____________________ so that they eventually developed into a well-rounded and highly productive team.

9. True, you did reply to the wisecrack, but I hardly regard "Not!" as an outstanding example of devastating ____________________.

10. Problems such as overcrowding, traffic congestion, and air pollution are more common in big cities than they are in less ____________________ areas.

11. How can we continue to live in this ____________________ atmosphere of suspicion and hatred?

12. Though her career in the movies had many ups and downs over the years, it reached its ____________________ when she won an Academy Award.

13. Our purpose is to help people in trouble, not to ____________________ out justice like a court of law.

14. You can't hope to hold a fruitful conversation if you are so ____________________ that you issue pronouncements instead of offering opinions.

15. They possess the kind of unshakable ____________________ that not only precludes lying but also requires them to express the truth, no matter what.

16. There are so many ____________________ elements in her personality that I find it difficult to tell you what kind of person she is.

17. The lower end of the ridge had been somewhat ____________________ by the action of glacial erosion many thousands of years ago.

18. ____________________ of your remarks on the probable effect of the law, may I quote from the column of a well-known political commentator?

19. Although the author's conclusions are open to debate, the scholarship upon which they are based is ____________________.

20. After the noisy excitement of the big party, the eerie silence that suddenly ____________________ seemed unnatural and difficult to accept.

Writing: Words in Action

1. Look back at "A Gap Year Makes Sense" (pages 174–175). Suppose you are a senior in high school and have decided to take a "gap year." Write an essay, in the form of a letter or email to your family or friends, in which you explain your choice and describe your plans for the next year. Use at least three details from the passage and three unit words.

2. Recently, there has been new interest in creating robust apprenticeship programs for young people who either delay going to college or who choose not to go to college. Do you think there should be more apprenticeship programs and/or a greater number of professional choices for young people after high school? Support your opinion with specific examples from your studies, reading (refer to pages 174–175), or personal observations and experience. Write at least three paragraphs, and use three or more words from this unit.

Vocabulary in Context

Literary Text

*The following excerpts are from works by Jonathan Swift. Some of the words you have studied in this unit appear in **boldface** type. Complete each statement below the excerpt by circling the letter of the correct answer.*

1. The captain persuaded me to accept a suit of clothes newly made; but I would not suffer the tailor to take my measure; however, Don Pedro being almost of my size, they fitted me well enough. He **accoutred** me with other necessaries, all new, which I aired for twenty-four hours before I would use them. (*Gulliver's Travels*)

To be **accoutred** is to be

a. supported **c.** decorated
b. chagrined **d.** equipped

Lemuel Gulliver is shipwrecked on Lilliput in *Gulliver's Travels.*

2. The garret windows and tops of houses were so crowded with spectators, that I thought in all my travels I had not seen a more **populous** place. (*Gulliver's Travels*)

A **populous** place has a lot of

a. diversion **c.** people
b. appeal **d.** scenery

3. That the other part of the parliament consisted of an assembly called the House of Commons, who were all principal gentlemen, freely picked and **culled** out by the people ... (*Gulliver's Travels*)

To be **culled** out is to be

a. selected **c.** rejected
b. isolated **d.** primed

4. I know a great officer of the army, who will sit for some time with a supercilious and impatient silence, full of anger and contempt for those who are talking; at length of a sudden demand audience; decide the matter in a short **dogmatical** way; then withdraw ... (*The Battle of the Books*—"Hints Towards an Essay on Conversation")

Something **dogmatical** is NOT

a. peremptory **c.** inflexible
b. adamant **d.** compromising

5. Raillery is the finest part of conversation; but, as it is our usual custom to counterfeit and adulterate whatever is too dear for us, so we have done with this, and turned it all into what is generally called **repartee**, or being smart ... (*The Battle of the Books*—"Hints Towards an Essay on Conversation")

Repartee is

a. oratory **c.** mischief
b. badinage **d.** gossip

Snap the code, or go to **vocabularyworkshop.com**

UNIT 15

*Read the following selection, taking note of the **boldface** words and their contexts. These words are among those you will be studying in Unit 15. As you complete the exercises in this unit, it may help to refer to the way the words are used below.*

Justice for the *Amistad*

<Newspaper Article>

Washington, D.C., *Mar. 2, 1841*—With the *Amistad* case soon to hear a decision from that **apotheosis** of American justice, the United States Supreme Court, we **adumbrate** here the essentials of the case for our readers.

Two years ago, in the summer of 1839, the Spanish schooner *Amistad*, sailing along the Cuban coast, was the scene of a slave mutiny led by one Joseph Cinqué. The 57 captives on board, having unburdened themselves of their shackles by means of a secreted iron file, killed the ship's captain, took control of the vessel, and demanded return passage to their native Africa. **Beguiled** by the ship's navigator, the mutineers were instead led northward, until the *Amistad* was seized by the USS *Washington* off the Long Island coast.

The plight of these men has generated great interest among abolitionists, who quote the proverb, "Oppression causeth rebellion." Under the stewardship of Lewis Tappan, a prominent New York City merchant, the Amistad Committee has raised money and attracted expertise for the legal defense of the captives. Its members have publicly **fulminated** against the injustices suffered by those men, by most accounts a veritable **jeremiad** of sorrows.

Thanks in part to the Committee's efforts, Messrs. Ruiz and Montez, the Cuban slave traders and subjects of the Spanish crown who were transporting the captives aboard the *Amistad*, are now perceived by many as **opportunists** possessed of a marked cruelty and **hauteur**.

At trial in a Connecticut District Court, agents of the Amistad Committee sought to **exculpate** the so-called mutineers on the grounds that they had been transported from Africa to Cuba illegally, in **contumacious** violation of international agreements outlawing the slave trade across the Atlantic. To **complement** this intention, they charged Ruiz and Montez with assault, kidnapping, and false imprisonment. Ruiz and Montez, in turn, have maintained that the captives are slaves and their own rightful property. The latter claim won quick support from the government of Spain.

The Connecticut court agreed that the transport of the slaves was illegal. It further declared that they were, therefore, not slaves at all but free men, kidnapped and held against their will, and within their rights to use force to defend their liberty. The court found, moreover, that Ruiz and Montez had made

Joseph Cinqué

Death of Capt. Ferrer, the Captain of the Amistad, July, 1839.

disingenuous claims affirming that the captives were born in Cuba, which is to say, on this side of the Atlantic. That false affirmation could have been naught but an **unconscionable** and willful misrepresentation of the facts. Accordingly, the District Court ruled that the *Amistad* captives were not the property of the Spanish traders and should be freed.

Evidently dissatisfied with the District Court's ruling, the federal government appealed the decision. By now the matter has worked its way up to this nation's highest court, where yesterday, after two days of legal arguments on behalf of both the *Amistad* captives and the United States government, John Quincy Adams, esteemed former President of the United States, arose to speak in defense of the captives.

The President emeritus began with a **didactic** characterization of Justice, as of necessity entailing equal regard for the rights of each individual. The atmosphere of the courtroom grew somber as the speech proceeded. On the whole it contained little of the **fustian** and fluff that betimes overburden such orations.

Mr. Adams did not **inhibit** himself from criticizing the actions of the Executive branch, but took aim at the administration, including President Van Buren himself.

Whether his argument moved the Justices will be soon known. The Supreme Court is expected to hand down its decision within the next fortnight, after hearing closing arguments from the Attorney General.

Snap the code, or go to **vocabularyworkshop.com**

Note the spelling, pronunciation, part(s) of speech, and definition(s) of each of the following words. Then write the word in the blank spaces in the illustrative sentence(s) following. Finally, study the lists of synonyms and antonyms.

1. adumbrate (ad′ əm brāt)

(*v.*) to outline or sketch broadly; to foreshadow or prefigure; to disclose partially

Writers often ________________ key ideas right away and then elaborate on them later.

SYNONYM: indicate

2. apotheosis (ə poth ē ō′ sis)

(*n.*) the elevation of a person to a divine rank or status; the glorification of a person as an ideal; a glorified ideal

Medieval knights were fierce warriors, but in literature they are presented as the ________________ of chivalry.

SYNONYM: deification

3. ascetic (ə set′ ik)

(*adj.*) practicing self-denial for the sake of personal or spiritual discipline; (*n.*) one who leads a life of self-discipline, especially to express religious devotion

Some artists and writers may find it beneficial to lead an ________________ life free of distractions.

The life of an ________________ supposedly repays the sacrifice of worldly things with spiritual rewards.

SYNONYMS: (*adj.*) spartan; (*n.*) celibate
ANTONYMS: (*adj.*) wanton; (*n.*) hedonist

4. bauble (bô′ bəl)

(*n.*) a small, showy ornament of little value or use

I found a rather valuable piece of vintage costume jewelry among the ________________ at the yard sale.

SYNONYMS: trifle, gewgaw, bagatelle
ANTONYMS: gem, precious jewel

5. beguile (bi gīl′)

(*v.*) to mislead or deceive; to cheat; to divert; to cause to vanish unnoticed

Many travelers choose to ________________ away the long hours of a journey with an absorbing book.

SYNONYMS: delude, dupe, lure

6. burgeon (bər′ jən)

(*v.*) to put forth new buds, leaves, or greenery; to develop rapidly or suddenly

Though it was still winter according to the calendar, our garden ________________ in the warm, sunny weather.

SYNONYMS: sprout, blossom, bloom
ANTONYMS: atrophy, shrivel, diminish

7. complement (kom′ plə mənt)

(*n.*) something that completes a whole; the quantity or number needed to make up a whole; the full number or allowance; (*v.*) to complete

The full ____________________ of dignitaries was present for the President's State of the Union Address.

She chose a hat that ____________________ her new outfit.

SYNONYMS: (*n.*) balance; (*v.*) round out

8. contumacious (kon tü mā′ shəs)

(*adj.*) obstinately or willfully disobedient; openly rebellious

Teenagers who are eager to assert their independence may become quite ____________________ at times.

SYNONYMS: impudent, unruly, defiant, refractory
ANTONYMS: docile, meek, deferential, cooperative

9. curmudgeon (kər məj′ ən)

(*n.*) an irascible, churlish person

No matter how hard we try, nothing we do seems to please our ____________________ of a boss.

SYNONYMS: crank, sorehead, churl

10. didactic (dī dak′ tik)

(*adj.*) intended to instruct, especially morally; inclined to moralize too much

At its best, children's literature teaches values, making it ____________________ as well as entertaining.

SYNONYMS: educational, instructional

11. disingenuous (dis in jen′ yü əs)

(*adj.*) lacking in sincerity or candor

____________________ individuals sometimes betray themselves in the very act of trying to appear sincere.

SYNONYMS: artful, sly, two-faced, insincere
ANTONYMS: candid, frank, artless, sincere

12. exculpate (ek′ skəl pāt)

(*v.*) to clear of guilt or blame

"I will present irrefutable evidence," the lawyer declared, "that will ____________________ my client."

SYNONYMS: absolve, acquit
ANTONYMS: convict, condemn

13. faux pas (fō pä′)

(*n.*) a slip in manners or conduct; a social blunder

No sooner had I arrived at the party than I embarrassed myself by committing a dreadful ____________________.

SYNONYM: indiscretion
ANTONYM: tour de force

14. fulminate (ful′ mə nāt)

(*v.*) to denounce or condemn vehemently; to explode, detonate

The senator proceeded to ____________________ against foreign commitments and entanglements.

SYNONYM: inveigh
ANTONYMS: praise, applaud, commend, extol

15. fustian (fəs′ chən)

(*n.*) inflated or pretentious language in speech or writing; a cloth made of cotton and flax

Although the politician's speech was filled with bombast and ____________________, it was devoid of substance.

SYNONYMS: rant, claptrap, bombast, grandiloquence

16. hauteur (hô tûr′)

(*n.*) haughtiness of bearing or attitude

His cold ____________________ and disdainful attitude made him extremely unpopular with his colleagues.

SYNONYMS: conceit, superciliousness, snobbishness
ANTONYMS: modesty, humility, diffidence, mousiness

17. inhibit (in hib′ it)

(*v.*) to restrain or hold back; to hinder or arrest; to prohibit

Poor eating habits may ____________________ a young person's physical development.

SYNONYMS: repress, check, suppress
ANTONYMS: foster, promote, expedite, facilitate

18. jeremiad (jer ə mī′ əd)

(*n.*) an elaborate or prolonged lamentation; any tale of woe

When asked about their sad plights, talk show guests often launch into tearful ____________________.

ANTONYMS: paean, song of praise

19. opportunist (op ər tü′ nist)

(*n.*) one who makes a practice of taking advantage of circumstances to further his or her own self-interest, regardless of principles or ultimate consequences

____________________ tend to treat those who are not useful to them with callous indifference.

SYNONYMS: self-seeker, exploiter

20. unconscionable (ən kon′ shən ə bəl)

(*adj.*) not guided or restrained by conscience, prudence, or reason; unscrupulous; immoderate

Top management's looting of the employees' retirement fund can only be described as ____________________.

SYNONYMS: unjustifiable, indefensible, unforgivable
ANTONYMS: justifiable, reasonable, honorable

Choosing the Right Word

*Select the **boldface** word that better completes each sentence. You might refer to the selection on pages 184–185 to see how most of these words are used in context.*

1. In his farewell address, President Dwight D. Eisenhower (**adumbrated, exculpated**) the necessity to beware of the rise of the "military-industrial complex."

In his now famous 1961 farewell address, President Dwight D. Eisenhower warned of the growing power of the defense industry.

2. In a democracy we have no need to disguise the human failings of our leaders; we can respect them without (**beguiling, apotheosizing**) them.

3. The candidates underrate the electorate if they think they can win votes with that kind of antiquated (**curmudgeon, fustian**).

4. What disappointed me was not so much your failure to complete the job but your (**didactic, disingenuous**) efforts to avoid all responsibility for the debacle.

5. Even the innate talents of a Mozart or an Einstein cannot (**fulminate, burgeon**) unless the environment is favorable to their growth.

6. Unlike the Athenians, who delighted in luxury, the Spartans espoused the virtue of (**ascetic, fustian**) simplicity.

7. The speaker referred scornfully to the "hysterical (**jeremiads, hauteurs**) of the ecologists," but I believe that they are warning us of real dangers.

8. I must say that I agree with their (**inhibitions, fulminations**) against those who deface our public buildings with unsightly graffiti.

9. Your tactics prove that you are not just an (**opportunist, apotheosis**) but someone with a ruthless disregard for others.

10. You are too young to understand how the trials of life can transform a happy-go-lucky youth into a solitary (**bauble, curmudgeon**).

11. The situation was rapidly becoming intolerable because some of the club members were not merely uncooperative but positively (**contumacious, opportunist**).

12. You have written a(n) (**didactic, unconscionable**) novel with a wealth of authentic documentation, but you have forgotten to entertain your readers.

13. (**Beguiled, Burgeoned**) by high-pressure sales talk, I bought a car that I did not need, could not afford, and did not even know how to drive.

14. The author found it ironic that the novel he had tossed off in his youth as a mere (**bauble, complement**) came to be viewed as his masterpiece.

15. The aim of the new biography was to (**exculpate, inhibit**) its subject of charges that previous biographers had wrongfully pressed against him.

16. When you have been guilty of rude conduct, do not try to minimize your guilt by referring to the incident as a mere (**jeremiad, faux pas**).

17. Many historians believe those apparently minor incidents (**adumbrated, exculpated**) the great revolutionary uprising that occurred a few years later.

18. The monk is a famous (**ascetic, apotheosis**) who sometimes appears publicly to oppose wars.

19. They make an excellent team because his deftness in handling people effectively (**complements, adumbrates**) her remarkable executive abilities.

20. When I asked him if he could dance, he looked at me with supreme (**disingenuousness, hauteur**) and asked, "Could Caruso sing?"

21. The (**hauteur, apotheosis**) of the actor's career was probably when he had the opportunity to play King Lear on the London stage.

22. A full and glowing moon and two shooting stars were the perfect (**burgeons, complements**) to a romantic dinner for two alongside the river.

23. The ancient photograph showed my grandmother in her native Russian village, sporting a (**bauble, fustian**) jacket to protect her against the harsh autumn wind.

24. What is the basis for your statement that advertising costs account for an (**ascetic, unconscionable**) part of the retail price of many products?

25. Because you are usually a rather boisterous person, I was surprised by your (**ascetic, inhibited**) behavior at the party.

Synonyms

*Choose the word from this unit that is the same or most nearly the same in meaning as the **boldface** word or expression in the phrase. Write that word on the line. Use a dictionary if necessary.*

1. led an **austere** existence ______________________
2. **misled** unwary customers with vague promises ______________________
3. **outlined** their plans at a press conference ______________________
4. committed one **gaffe** after another ______________________
5. will **exonerate** them without further ado ______________________
6. **flourished** in that mild climate ______________________
7. **rails** against the government's policies ______________________
8. **knicknacks** that have great sentimental value ______________________
9. has a reputation for being a **grouch** ______________________
10. dismissed as **moralistic** by most literary critics ______________________

Antonyms

*Choose the word from this unit that is most nearly opposite in meaning to the **boldface** word or expression in the phrase. Write that word on the line. Use a dictionary if necessary.*

1. **treasure** discovered at the flea market ____________________
2. a **dissolute** and dishonorable scoundrel ____________________
3. a **Pollyanna** in the face of discouragement ____________________
4. her **discretion** at the meeting secured the contract ____________________
5. **withering** basil plant left unwatered ____________________

Completing the Sentence

From the words in this unit, choose the one that best completes each of the following sentences. Write the word in the space provided.

1. The editorial argues that the crime-fighting situation cannot improve until the police department receives its full ____________________ of personnel.

2. I wonder how many people have been taken in by those silly TV ads that attempt to pass off worthless ____________________ as valuable jewelry.

3. How could a person of your knowledge and experience allow herself to be ____________________ by vague promises and empty reassurances?

4. Her standards of proper behavior are so demanding that she regards every minor ____________________ as an unforgivable social offense.

5. What at first appeared to be no more than a rather favorable opinion of himself has ____________________ into unlimited conceit.

6. In a rather silly painting called *The* ____________________ *of Homer*, the artist attempts to show the blind poet's reception among the gods.

7. Successful politicians must be alert to every favorable circumstance, but if they are no more than ____________________, it is hard to see how they will ever accomplish anything worthwhile.

8. I won't go into that shop because the snooty salespeople treat me with the ____________________ and disdain of aristocrats dealing with their lackeys.

9. Instead of simply stating his case, he launched into an emotional appeal whose language degenerated into mere ____________________ and bombast.

10. Because there was no time to go into elaborate details, all that we could do was ____________________ the general features of the plan.

11. It is often more effective to offer a few just words of criticism than to _______________ long and loud against those who offend us.

12. While two of the accused were indicted on conspiracy charges, the third was eventually _______________ of any involvement in the plot.

13. What we need in this situation is not a lugubrious _______________ cataloging our troubles but a workable plan for improvements.

14. At first we thought that he was just pretending to be surly, but later we discovered that he really was a(n) _______________.

15. We all have aggressive impulses, but in most cases our early training and conditioning tend to _______________ the open expression of them.

16. I find it impossible to understand how the world can stand idly by while _______________ acts of cruelty are being committed daily.

17. After his conversion, the young man renounced his former profligacy and dissipation to lead the life of a(n) _______________.

18. For the eighteenth-century moralist, art and literature had an essentially _______________ purpose; they should teach as well as entertain.

19. The chairman of the Senate committee angrily threatened the witness with contempt charges because of her _______________ attitude.

20. Though your unwillingness to make me a small loan is disappointing, what infuriates me is your _______________ explanation that it is "for my own good."

Writing: Words in Action

1. Look back at "Justice for the *Amistad*" (pages 184–185). Ultimately, the Supreme Court ruled in 1841 that the captives should be freed and allowed to return to their home country. Using at least two details from the passage and three unit words, write an essay that summarizes the facts of the case and the reasons the justices ruled in favor of the captives.

2. Journalists often claim to be objective in their coverage of the news. Do you think it is possible—or even desirable—for a journalist to be objective when reporting on controversial or emotionally charged events? In a brief essay, support your opinion with specific examples from your studies, reading (refer to pages 184–185), or personal observations and experience. Write at least three paragraphs, and use three or more words from this unit.

Vocabulary in Context

Literary Text

*The following excerpts are from novels by Anthony Trollope. Some of the words you have studied in this unit appear in **boldface** type. Complete each statement below the excerpt by circling the letter of the correct answer.*

1. The people around her were gracious on the presumption that she was going to do as they wished, and would be quite prepared to withdraw their smiles should she prove to be **contumacious**. (*The American Senator*)

Someone who is **contumacious** is NOT

a. obstinate **c.** dissenting
b. submissive **d.** cheerful

2. It was, however, generally felt that, though Mr. Slow was the slowest in his speech, Mr. Bideawhile was the longest in getting anything said. Mr. Slow would often **beguile** his time with unnecessary remarks; but Mr. Bideawhile was so constant in **beguiling** his time, that men wondered how, in truth, he ever did anything at all. (*Miss Mackenzie*)

To **beguile** time is to

a. while away **c.** misunderstand
b. misuse **d.** forget

Anthony Trollope wrote 47 novels during his career by composing for three hours every morning before breakfast.

3. "Those lawyers can never understand that there can be anything of friendly feeling about money. They can't put friendly feelings into their **unconscionable** bills." (*Miss Mackenzie*)

Something **unconscionable** is

a. forgettable **c.** honorable
b. mediocre **d.** unreasonable

4. Sir John ... was almost wild with agony and anger. He threw up his hands with dismay as he walked along the passages of the Shadrach Office, and **fulminated** mental curses against the wasp that was able to sting him so deeply. (*Miss Mackenzie*)

To **fulminate** is to

a. whisper **c.** repress
b. rant **d.** justify

5. The man wrote back to say ... that he wanted his money at once. George Hotspur sent the man his money, not without many curses on the illiberality of such a **curmudgeon**. (*Sir Harry Hotspur of Humblethwaite*)

A **curmudgeon** is someone who is

a. surly **c.** ugly
b. kindly **d.** outrageous

Snap the code, or go to **vocabularyworkshop.com**

Vocabulary for Comprehension

*Read the following selection in which some of the words you have studied in Units 13–15 appear in **boldface** type. Then answer the questions on page 195.*

Even hazardous jobs have their satisfactions, as this passage makes clear.

(Line)

Birds aren't the only ones who can enjoy a bird's-eye view of things. The intrepid workers who wash the windows of skyscrapers and other (5) tall buildings share that lofty position.

Working hundreds of feet above the sidewalk is not for everybody, certainly not for anyone who is **inhibited** by a fear of heights. But (10) heights are just one of the hazards faced by window washers. **Mercurial** weather conditions also put workers at risk. They must learn to deal calmly and cautiously with wind and (15) rain and snow. They deserve our praise for their courage and the skill with which they do their difficult job.

Tall buildings have various kinds of windows. Some can be cleaned (20) while the worker stands inside the building. Others can be opened halfway or tilted inward and cleaned by leaning out while remaining inside. Still others cannot be opened (25) and must be cleaned from the outside. To do this, workers may have to stand on a narrow ledge or on a platform that is suspended by cables from a building's roof. (30) Workers wear safety harnesses that they secure to the window frames while they use their squeegees to clean the glass. Window washers also need gloves, safety goggles, (35) and respirator masks to protect them from caustic cleaning substances. Most important of all, they should always check their equipment before beginning work to make sure that (40) everything is in good condition and fastened securely.

People who become window washers generally do so of their own **volition**. They say that the perks of (45) the job outweigh the dangers. First of all there is the satisfaction of keeping windows **immaculate**. Then, of course, there are those bird's-eye views. Window washers can look out (50) over the **resplendent** tops of magnificent tall buildings gleaming in the sunlight and enjoy the panorama of the city.

1. The first paragraph (lines 1–5) introduces the passage's topic with
   a. an analogy
   b. a symbol
   c. an anecdote
   d. a statistic
   e. a quotation

2. The meaning of **inhibited** (line 9) is
   a. unconcerned
   b. prohibited
   c. held back
   d. made dizzy
   e. unnerved

3. **Mercurial** (line 11) most nearly means
   a. unseasonable
   b. predictable
   c. flighty
   d. harsh
   e. volatile

4. Based on the details cited by the writer in paragraph 2 (lines 6–17), which of the following pairs of qualities are most needed by window washers?
   a. compassion and restraint
   b. humility and politeness
   c. intelligence and a sense of humor
   d. calmness and caution
   e. foresight and initiative

5. According to the passage, all the following are related to window washers' safety EXCEPT
   a. equipment checks
   b. squeegees
   c. harnesses
   d. respirator masks
   e. goggles

6. The meaning of **volition** (line 44) is
   a. choice
   b. ability
   c. need
   d. compulsion
   e. whim

7. **Immaculate** (line 47) most nearly means
   a. safe
   b. faultless
   c. spotless
   d. soiled
   e. sealed

8. The main idea of paragraph 4 (lines 42–53) is that window washers
   a. have an artistic temperament
   b. are devoted to their work
   c. inevitably face accidents in such a dangerous job
   d. reap from their work satisfaction that outweighs the danger
   e. perform hazardous work for very low pay

9. At the end of the passage, which provides an echo of the introduction?
   a. mention of the importance of safety equipment
   b. a reference to unpredictable weather conditions
   c. a remark about everyday urban life
   d. mention of the sacrifices made by window washers
   e. a reference to bird's-eye views

10. **Resplendent** (line 50) is best defined as
    a. dazzling
    b. varied
    c. decorative
    d. dramatic
    e. grimy

11. Which best describes the writer's attitude toward the passage's subject?
    a. skeptical
    b. humorous
    c. enthusiastic
    d. informal
    e. critical

12. Which detail is NOT in the passage?
    a. how different windows are cleaned
    b. how much money window washers can earn
    c. the gear window washers use
    d. which hazards window washers face
    e. how window washers clean windows on skyscrapers

Two-Word Completions

Select the pair of words that best complete the meaning of each of the following passages.

1. During the Civil War, Robert E. Lee's freedom of choice was seriously ____________ by the fact that the South could never replace the losses it sustained through normal battlefield ____________.

a. palliated . . . volition
b. inhibited . . . attrition
c. truncated . . . convolution
d. adumbrated . . . imprecation

2. Years ago, all art had two ____________ purposes: "to point a moral or adorn a tale." Accordingly, no work was judged to be really complete if either the ____________ or the decorative element was not in evidence.

a. vestigial . . . dogmatic
b. ineluctable . . . licentious
c. complementary . . . didactic
d. unimpeachable . . . chauvinistic

3. "The man is not a disinterested observer of the passing scene," I said. "He is essentially a(n) ____________ who uses his column in the newspaper as a kind of soapbox from which to ____________ against the iniquities of those around him."

a. curmudgeon . . . exculpate
b. chauvinist . . . palliate
c. opportunist . . . truncate
d. polemicist . . . fulminate

4. During the election of 1860, the Democrats could not present a united front because the party was torn asunder by ____________ strife and petty regional ____________.

a. factional . . . bickering
b. contumacious . . . attrition
c. dogmatic . . . repartee
d. unconscionable . . . vainglory

5. The last ____________ of the previous century's iron ore mining industry are apparent in that tiny Michigan ghost town that today is one attraction, among many, in the state's ____________ tourism industry.

a. vestiges . . . burgeoning
b. probities . . . supervening
c. factionalisms . . . stigmatizing
d. jeremiads . . . hauteur

6. Without conscious ____________, after years of living in abundance and in an overpopulated city, she finally pursued a simple and ____________ life in a tiny cabin with a small patch of farmland.

a. convolution . . . licentious
b. repartee . . . ineluctable
c. volition . . . ascetic
d. imprecation . . . acerbic

7. Even the young preschool children were unimpressed by the new teacher's ____________ and clichéd advice—and they were utterly exasperated by his ____________ and inflexible approach to instruction.

a. resplendent . . . noxious
b. immaculate . . . mercurial
c. polemics . . . truncated
d. bromides . . . dogmatic

In the passage "A Gap Year Makes Sense" (see pages 174–175), the writer points out that today's high school students are "burning the candle at both ends." The meaning of this phrase may not be obvious, as it means something different from the literal meanings of the individual words within it.

In fact, this phrase is an **idiom**. In the unit opener passage, it means staying up late and getting up early in order to get a lot of work done, requiring artificial light at both "ends" of the day.

Choosing the Right Idiom

Read each sentence. Use context clues to figure out the meaning of each idiom in ***boldface*** *print. Then write the letter of the definition for the idiom in the sentence.*

1. Let's **get this straight**. You have the flu and a very high fever. You are not going to work today. ________
2. We need to get this **in black and white** so that you can get started hiring your staff. ________
3. My best advice to you is to **mind your Ps and Qs**. Your grandparents are from a different generation. ________
4. It is clear you didn't want to see this movie. **Give it a rest** and now just try to enjoy yourself. ________
5. This is, **hands down**, the greatest lasagna I've ever eaten. What is the secret ingredient? ________
6. Sure, I would **toe the line** for this corporation if someone would assure me a livable wage. ________
7. The leaders were worried that the poor trade deal would make them **lose face** and thus anger the citizens. ________
8. Our financial team acted unquestionably **above board** and so our records are spotless. ________
9. She refuses to **lie low**; the punitive action, in fact, has made her even more outspoken. ________
10. This is his last month on the job—our manager wants to **phone it in** and doesn't care who's affected. ________

a. stop talking about, or doing, something annoying

b. be humiliated

c. avoid attention and notice

d. in writing or in print; make official

e. do a task with little effort or enthusiasm

f. behave yourself and don't offend anyone

g. accept the rules and authority of a group

h. open and honest; without fraud

i. make something clear and reach an understanding

j. easily; without question

Writing with Idioms

Find the meaning of each idiom. (Use an online or print dictionary if necessary.) Then write a sentence for each idiom.

1. knock me over with a feather

2. go for broke

3. diamond in the rough

4. strike a chord

5. make a beeline for

6. sitting duck

7. take a hard line

8. Jack of all trades and master of none

9. come apart at the seams

10. not for love or money

11. at sixes and sevens

12. wear more than one hat

Denotation and Connotation

The definition of a word is its **denotation**; it is objective and found in the dictionary. There are many words, however, that have one or more subjective meanings. These are the word's **connotations**, and they can be positive or negative.

By using words with slightly different meanings and connotations, writers can establish a precise idea or mood. For example, to convey that a character is in a difficult situation, a writer might describe him or her as *dejected* or *miserable*. To convey an additional sense of powerlessness for the character, a writer might describe him or her as *downtrodden* or *hapless*.

Now examine these synonyms for the word *beguile*:

enchant *charm* *seduce* *ensnare*

Enchant and *charm* have positive connotations, while *beguile*, indicating some level of deception, can be used both positively and negatively. In contrast, the more negative *seduce* suggests that there is premeditation. *Ensnare* suggests both premeditation as well as malice.

Think: A mother enchants her children with tales of the tooth fairy, while a get-rich-quick scheme seduces or ensnares an unwary investor.

Review these words with similar denotations but different connotations.

NEUTRAL	POSITIVE	NEGATIVE
opinionated	**decisive**	**dogmatic**
populous	**abundant**	**overrun**
informative	**enlightening**	**didactic**

Understanding and then skillfully using a word's denotation and its connotations are important ways to get the most out of what you read and to perfect your writing.

Shades of Meaning

Write a plus sign (+) in the box if the word has a positive connotation. Write a minus sign (–) if the word has a negative connotation. Put a zero (0) if the word is neutral.

1. adumbrate ☐	**2.** contumacious ☐	**3.** curmudgeon ☐	**4.** cull ☐
5. repartee ☐	**6.** licentious ☐	**7.** apropos ☐	**8.** mercurial ☐
9. accolade ☐	**10.** protocol ☐	**11.** apotheosis ☐	**12.** fustian ☐
13. fulminate ☐	**14.** unconscionable ☐	**15.** complement ☐	**16.** acerbity ☐

WORD STUDY

Expressing the Connotation

Read each sentence. Select the word in parentheses that expresses the connotation (positive, negative, or neutral) given at the beginning of the sentence.

negative **1.** The (**callousness, faux pas**) of the host made the guests feel somewhat uncomfortable.

negative **2.** He spray-painted the bookshelves inside, and then (**noxious, unpleasant**) fumes filled the apartment.

positive **3.** The invention of the computer might be the (**apogee, peak**) of twentieth-century developments.

neutral **4.** The night sky, (**bright, resplendent**) with stars, was unlike any I'd ever seen before.

negative **5.** Your (**bromides, placations**) have generated even more bad feelings among the club members.

neutral **6.** The country's future is threatened by internal (**factionalism, enmity**).

negative **7.** His (**chauvinist, biased**) statement reveals decades of a backward and poorly funded educational system.

positive **8.** The child (**burgeoned, matured**) after spending the summer in the sophisticated metropolis.

Challenge: Using Connotation

Choose vocabulary words from Units 13–15 to replace the highlighted words in the sentences below. Then explain how the connotation of the replacement word changes the tone of the sentence.

disingenuous	**exculpating**	**ascetic**
inhibiting	**opportunist**	**jeremiad**

1. I find your presence **stifling** ____________________. In order to get my work done, I'll have to go to the library to be alone.

____

____

2. By definition, the nation-state acts as a(n) **exploiter** ____________________ in addition to acting in its own self-interest.

____

____

3. My brother's **duplicitous** ____________________ behavior confused me and led me to believe he was getting along well at school.

____

____

Classical Roots

temp—time

This Latin root appears in **contretemps** (page 176), which means "an inopportune or embarrassing mishap." Some other words based on the same root are listed below.

contemplative	**extempore**	**temperance**	**tempest**
contemporaneous	**temperamentally**	**temperature**	**tempestuous**

From the list of words above, choose the one that corresponds to each of the brief definitions below. Write the word in the blank space in the illustrative sentence below the definition.

1. existing or occurring at the same period of time

The lives of writers Christopher Marlowe and Sir Walter Raleigh were ______________ with that of William Shakespeare.

2. a violent storm; a tumult, uproar

The small fishing boat foundered in the raging ______________.

3. the degree of hotness or coldness in a body or an environment; the specific degree of hotness or coldness as measured on a scale

The parents worried when the baby continued to run a high ______________ for three days.

4. stormy; violent; turbulent

Their ______________ relationship ended when the stress became too much to bear.

5. by nature, disposition; moodily; impulsively

Although she had always dreamed of being an investigative journalist, she soon realized that she was ______________ unsuited for the job.

6. moderation, self-restraint; total abstinence from alcohol

My brother, a cautious person, follows the path of ______________ in all areas of life.

7. inclined to consider intently, thoughtful; meditative; pensive

Rodin's famed sculpture *The Thinker* shows a man sitting in a(n) ______________ pose.

8. in an impromptu, unrehearsed manner; on the spur of the moment

After hearing the mayor's disturbing statement, an irate citizen delivered a rebuttal ______________.

Synonyms

Select the two words or expressions that are most nearly the same in meaning.

1. a. immaculate **b.** spotless **c.** sagacious **d.** salubrious
2. a. ambivalent **b.** lugubrious **c.** determined **d.** mournful
3. a. adumbrate **b.** beleaguer **c.** outline **d.** ponder
4. a. expression **b.** contretemps **c.** faux pas **d.** apogee
5. a. forte **b.** interest **c.** acerbity **d.** strength
6. a. complement **b.** nullify **c.** complete **d.** cozen
7. a. memory **b.** herald **c.** harbinger **d.** debauch
8. a. lexicon **b.** divination **c.** time frame **d.** vocabulary
9. a. confusion **b.** split **c.** schism **d.** emolument
10. a. satire **b.** claque **c.** persiflage **d.** banter
11. a. prescience **b.** panache **c.** foresight **d.** determination
12. a. picaresque **b.** passive **c.** supine **d.** uncooperative
13. a. peccadillo **b.** melee **c.** crisis **d.** fight
14. a. morass **b.** swamp **c.** collection **d.** syndrome
15. a. lucubration **b.** delay **c.** thought **d.** solecism

Antonyms

Select the two words that are most nearly opposite in meaning.

16. a. oblique **b.** disparate **c.** identical **d.** effete
17. a. intellectual **b.** practicable **c.** quixotic **d.** ancillary
18. a. minuscule **b.** contumelious **c.** trained **d.** gargantuan
19. a. youthful **b.** inchoate **c.** plebeian **d.** patrician
20. a. affinity **b.** obloquy **c.** acclaim **d.** volition
21. a. microcosm **b.** embezzlement **c.** metamorphosis **d.** macrocosm
22. a. foreign **b.** malleable **c.** inflexible **d.** noxious
23. a. obfuscate **b.** pander **c.** coalesce **d.** clarify
24. a. paean **b.** pastiche **c.** criticism **d.** liturgy
25. a. considerate **b.** maladroit **c.** dexterous **d.** parlous

Analogies

Select the item that best completes the comparison.

26. **chimerical** is to **skepticism** as
    a. indigenous is to surprise
    b. noisome is to disgust
    c. bigotry is to chivalry
    d. sanguine is to contempt

27. **éclat** is to **French** as
    a. bathos is to German
    b. bête noire is to Spanish
    c. virtuoso is to Italian
    d. fustian is to Portuguese

28. **prolix** is to **wordiness** as
    a. queasy is to contentment
    b. portentous is to happiness
    c. mellifluous is to acidity
    d. hedonism is to pleasure seeking

29. **marauder** is to **depredations** as
    a. lackey is to daydreams
    b. incubus is to nightmares
    c. nemesis is to revels
    d. protégé is to plaudits

30. **fervid** is to **enthusiasm** as
    a. ecumenical is to anger
    b. refractory is to compliance
    c. cantankerous is to irritability
    d. lackluster is to delight

31. **obsequies** is to **somber** as
    a. funerals is to mercurial
    b. peace talks is to martial
    c. battles is to jovial
    d. revels is to saturnalian

32. **hoi polloi** is to **Greek** as
    a. dictum is to Hebrew
    b. quid pro quo is to Latin
    c. genre is to German
    d. cul-de-sac is to Spanish

33. **virtuoso** is to **masterful** as
    a. parsimonious is to liberality
    b. aberration is to apropos
    c. heyday is to regret
    d. anachronism is to outdated

Two-Word Completions

Select the word pair from among the choices given.

34. I don't mean to ____________ you, but your constant annoying behavior has made you the ____________ of my existence!
    a. auger . . . bellwether
    b. bode . . . curmudgeon
    c. browbeat . . . bane
    d. impinge . . . bromide

35. Far from solving the problem, all we've done is offer a(n) ____________ of ____________ attempts at a solution.
    a. charisma . . . execrable
    b. didactic . . . de facto
    c. cognate . . . iconoclastic
    d. plethora . . . abortive

36. The disaster was such a(n) ____________ that I couldn't help but let out a(n) ____________ of despair.
    a. cataclysm . . . caterwaul
    b. interstice . . . icon
    c. enclave . . . cull
    d. liaison . . . remand

37. The ____________ of the leadership of this organization will seemingly never change; people seem to have a(n) ____________ attitude toward new candidates for office.
    a. hierarchy . . . hidebound
    b. empathy . . . contumacious
    c. pundit . . . systemic
    d. purview . . . insouciant

Supplying Words in Context

To complete each sentence, select the best word from among the choices given. Not all words in the word bank will be used. You may modify the word form as necessary.

philippic	**resplendent**	**flamboyant**	**deracinate**
abeyance	**foray**	**touchstone**	**fait accompli**
bruit	**aegis**	**gothic**	**internecine**
nihilism	**viable**	**imbue**	**folderol**

38. His bitter disapproval led him to deliver a ____________________ during the trial.

39. The dark and gloomy plot marked the reading selection as part of the ____________________ school of literature.

40. Her sweeping criticism of the social order was indicative of the ____________________ of her philosophy.

41. The performer was so ____________________ that he brought to mind a showy peacock.

42. The conflict is ____________________: All parties involved will suffer.

43. You should seek to ____________________ your bad habits as you would remove a rotten tree stump from the yard.

nepotism	**bowdlerize**	**bilious**	**disparity**
gambol	**sacrosanct**	**polarize**	**opt**
fetid	**labyrinth**	**homily**	**ensconce**
carte blanche	**tendentious**	**elixir**	**philistine**

44. He appointed his nephew to the new position; it was a clear case of ____________________.

45. The ____________________ was so complicated and circuitous that I feared we wouldn't find our way out.

46. I was given ____________________ to choose whatever method I wanted.

47. His ____________________ reaction made plain his disgust.

48. In the fairy tale, the magic ____________________ caused the princess to fall asleep for a hundred years.

49. Grandpa offered a short ____________________ explaining his attitude toward life.

Word Associations

*Select the word or expression that best completes the meaning of the sentence or answers the question, with particular reference to the meaning of the word in **boldface** type.*

50. Deeds of **derring-do** are associated particularly with
- **a.** knights-errant
- **b.** politicians
- **c.** suburban commuters
- **d.** scholars and intellectuals

51. Which of the following indicates **kudos**?
- **a.** "Get out of my life!"
- **b.** "Do what I say, not what I do."
- **c.** "What have I done to deserve this?"
- **d.** "You're the greatest!"

52. An **empirical** analysis of a problem is based primarily on
- **a.** the laws of chance
- **b.** preconceived ideas
- **c.** wishful thinking
- **d.** experience

53. If you refer to someone's reactions as **maudlin**, you are
- **a.** expressing sympathy
- **b.** complaining of excessive sentimentality
- **c.** showing utter indifference
- **d.** charging deliberate misrepresentation

54. Your situation might well be described as **precarious** if you were
- **a.** hanging from the edge of a cliff
- **b.** lolling in a hammock
- **c.** playing tennis with a weak opponent
- **d.** attending the Senior Prom

55. What advice might you give to a person who is guilty of a **tautology**?
- **a.** "See your doctor immediately."
- **b.** "Don't repeat yourself."
- **c.** "Stop that abusive language."
- **d.** "Speak more slowly and distinctly."

56. A person who has just received a **lagniappe** would most likely
- **a.** take some medication
- **b.** mend his or her ways
- **c.** seek revenge
- **d.** say, "Thanks!"

57. From a renowned **raconteur** you would expect
- **a.** a superb dinner
- **b.** an entertaining story
- **c.** expert legal advice
- **d.** the perfect crime

58. The expression "**vicissitudes** of life" refers to life's
- **a.** beginning and end
- **b.** pleasures
- **c.** ups and downs
- **d.** side issues

59. People who are affected by **xenophobia** are
- **a.** fond of rich food
- **b.** afraid of heights
- **c.** suspicious of foreigners
- **d.** unlucky in love

60. We would expect **aficionados** of the opera to
- **a.** picket the local opera house
- **b.** attend opera performances often
- **c.** sing the lead role in *Carmen*
- **d.** never go to an opera

61. People who indulge in **casuistry** are most likely
- **a.** overeating
- **b.** spreading rumors
- **c.** splitting hairs
- **d.** feeling sorry for themselves

Choosing the Right Meaning

Read each sentence carefully. Then select the item that best completes the statement below the sentence.

62. I think that such a menial job is not **commensurate** with my abilities and education.
The word **commensurate** most nearly means
a. corresponding **b.** appositive **c.** adjunct **d.** victorious

63. The emotions expressed in the poem run the **gamut** from sheer exhilaration to unimaginable despair.
The word **gamut** most nearly means
a. range **b.** beatitude **c.** analogy **d.** corollary

64. The idea that we would fall for such an obvious ruse was **risible**.
The word **risible** is best defined as
a. expensive **b.** equal **c.** laughable **d.** ineffable

65. It was only a brief **vignette**, but nonetheless it was revealing of the character's strong sense of right and wrong.
The word **vignette** most nearly means
a. matrix **b.** poltroon **c.** respite **d.** anecdote

66. The terrible storm was a **traumatic** event for the entire community.
The word **traumatic** most nearly means
a. waggish **b.** naughty **c.** jolting **d.** ribald

67. They demand quiet in the museum so please ask members of your group to **modulate** their voices.
The word **modulate** most nearly means
a. refer **b.** soften **c.** truckle **d.** inveigle

68. Perhaps you can use a **mnemonic** to help you remember the events.
The word **mnemonic** most nearly means
a. vassal **b.** tempest **c.** cue **d.** persona

69. As a welcoming gesture, the restaurant offers an appetizer **gratis**.
The word **gratis** is best defined as
a. pleasant **b.** free **c.** tasty **d.** prurient

70. The soft light of dawn filtered through the **diaphanous** curtains.
The word **diaphanous** is best defined as
a. pragmatic **b.** lamentable **c.** translucent **d.** oblivious

WORD LIST

The following is a list of all the words taught in the Units of this book. The number after each entry indicates the page on which the word is defined.

INDEX